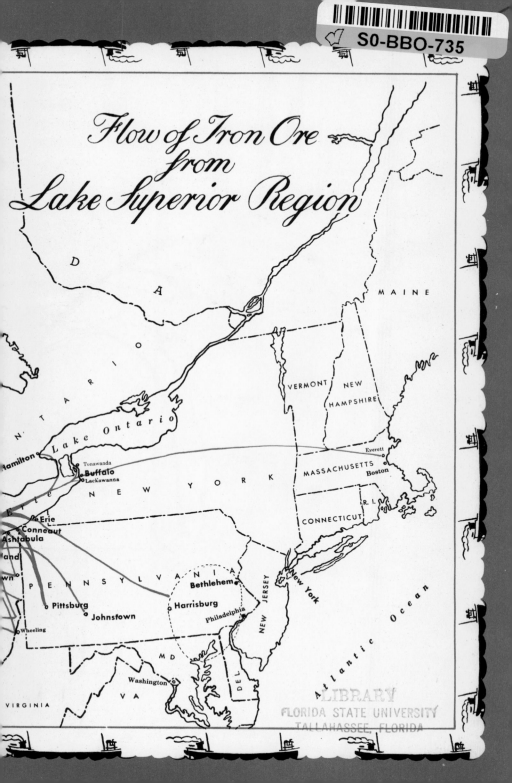

Flow of Iron Ore
from
Lake Superior Region

A CENTURY OF IRON AND MEN

PICK-AND-SHOVEL PERIOD, JACKSON MINE, 1860

A
CENTURY
of
IRON and MEN

by Harlan Hatcher

●

ILLUSTRATED

●

THE BOBBS-MERRILL COMPANY, INC.

INDIANAPOLIS   *Publishers*   NEW YORK

COPYRIGHT, 1950, BY THE BOBBS-MERRILL COMPANY, INC.

PRINTED IN THE UNITED STATES OF AMERICA

First Edition

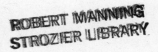

To

WILLIAM GWINN MATHER

and the memory of

SAMUEL LIVINGSTON MATHER

his father

who, in succession, with the same company, provided continuous leadership in the development
of the Lake Superior iron-ore mines through
the first full century of their vital production.

CONTENTS

LIST OF ILLUSTRATIONS

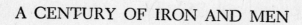

A CENTURY OF IRON AND MEN

1

ALONG THE GREAT LAKES SHIPPING LANE

THE Cleveland-Cliffs lake freighter *Pontiac* steams out of Lake Erie into the channel of the Conneaut River at Conneaut. She is loaded deep with 12,000 tons of iron ore from Marquette. She comes on up the river and eases to a landing alongside the ore dock under the towering Hulett unloaders. The crew has already opened the hatches. The minute she is secured the giant open jaws of the Hulett unloaders descend, one after another, rhythmically into the hold and begin to empty the ship by closing on 17 tons of ore at a bite. They rise vertically with their burden, swing it almost daintily over to the enclosed chute and release it into the waiting cars to be hauled off to the steel mills of Pittsburgh or the Mahoning Valley. In less than four hours she is scraped clean and riding high. There is no coal for her in September 1949 because of the strike. She takes on water ballast to go up light. Two waiting tugs come up, secure their lines fore and aft, and ease her around in the turning basin that seems just wide enough to accommodate her

580-foot length. She backs up to the coal wharf and takes on fuel for the return voyage. As night falls over the harbor, she gets under way and glides down the channel, among the little fishing boats with flash lights, and out past the lighthouse into the open lake.

She steams through the night across Lake Erie. Off to port the harbor lights flash and the lights of the shore cities—Conneaut, Ashtabula, Fairport, then Cleveland—glow against the dark sky across the choppy waters. The freighter slips along as silently as a canoe and without vibration in the texas house. At daybreak she is entering the Detroit River, threading her way confidently among the buoys past the lighthouse into the Amherstburg Channel. All day she steams up the narrow crowded channels: past the miles of Detroit industries on the banks of the Detroit River, under the Ambassador Bridge, past the skyscrapers of downtown Detroit, where the mail boat comes alongside to take and deliver the mail, round Belle Isle to Livingstone Light, across the dredged channel in the wide St. Clair Flats, up the narrow winding river, signaling passing ships with a blast from her deep-toned whistle, under the Blue Water Bridge and out into the open waters of Lake Huron.

Dinner of the best food is served to the officers and crew in the dining room in the after house, and a flock of gulls soar and dip to seize the gobbets thrown over the side from the galley. And before one can take three turns along the wire-cable rail around the battened-down hatches, night again falls. The running lights of down-bound ships shine across the lake, and the plume of smoke of the freighter ahead of us in the long procession from the Lake Erie ports to the Lake Superior docks is absorbed in the darkness. There is a light fog lying low over the surface of Lake Huron and the captain in the pilothouse flips on the new radar to port of the wheel. The screen fogs over, then clears, and there, in miniature, appear the outlines of the shore four miles to the west and the moving dots of light which show the 18 ships in our vicinity with their distances scaled off on the screen.

Below the pilothouse, in the observation lounge, the marine radio brings in the news from the big outside world to the self-contained little world of the ship.

We sleep quietly and in peace through the night. On the morning of the second day the ship crosses the wide opening of the Straits of Mackinac and enters the buoy-marked channel of the St. Marys River. It is a marvel that the big, long ship manages to negotiate all the sharp turns in the cramped and crowded river with such precision and such ease and grace. She swings so sharply at some bends that the captain must sight back over her stern on the ranges in the clearings on the hillside to direct her on her course. Yet she keeps in her allotted traffic lane as though she were a motorcar running along a highway between white lines.

It is late afternoon when she rounds the bend into the basin below the locks at the Sault. The ship-to-shore telephone rings in the pilothouse. It is Cleveland calling—as though this were an office in the Union Commerce Building. The captain also talks to the officer of the Sault locks and receives signals and directions to enter the first lock to the east. A down-bound ship is locking through and the *Pontiac*, unable to idle long enough, has to cast lines and tie up for a few minutes while she waits her turn. Then she eases her huge bulk expertly into the lock, the gates close, and in a few minutes, lifted 19 feet, she moves on up the canal and out into the St. Marys River as the second day fades over her journey. The low sun turns Canada's Sault Ste. Marie, with its office buildings and church towers spotlighted against the green backdrop of hills, into a vivid stage setting. A tremendous and vari-colored sunset flashes dramatically across the western sky. It reflects from the smokestacks of the steel mills that look as if they were floating on the water at the Falls.

The weather reports come in regularly. There is a storm on Lake Superior. It is chopping up Whitefish Bay and some ships have put in to harbor to wait better weather before venturing into the open waters. Rain squalls are visible on the radar screen a dozen miles ahead. The ship for the first time rolls, and the captain stays on at the open window of the pilothouse. The night is very rough. A glass in the bathroom is tossed to the floor. The captain orders more ballast. He sits at his desk in the pilothouse with the navigation chart spread out under the green-shaded light. He charts a course that will take him off his shortest route, but which will quarter the lash of the wind and waves. The giant ship rocks back and forth, rhyth-mically, like a hammock or a cradle. She rides out the storm in the early morning. The captain veers her course back west-southwest and heads her for Marquette. Morning of the third day finds her gliding along through calm waters under the sun and a clean sky. She is too far north to afford a clear view of the Pictured Rocks, but the glasses pick out the long high wall of the escarpment along the south shore. Grand Island is like a low-lying cloud, or a mist rising from the lake.

The bright midmorning sun over the stern lights up brilliantly the city of Marquette against its half circle of hills. It seems only a short distance away, but the light-house and the massive dark bulk of the ore docks are 12 miles straight ahead and we are an hour and a half away from landing. It is a striking scene, and we have ample time to contemplate it and its century of history before we enter the harbor channel at reduced speed. The ship seems almost to drift along among the buoys as she swings round at a right angle and eases up to the mammoth dock. We move carefully, for ships have been lost here on the rocks when they have swung a few feet too far. Another ship is loading at the dock. She, too, is a giant, but she is dwarfed by the vast battery of ore pockets out of which tons of ore stream into her hold. With another demon-stration of uncanny skill, without the help of tugs, the captain places his ship alongside the loading freighter, clearing the other boat by inches all along her 600-foot length, and brings his ship to as carefully and gently as though he were placing a child in its crib.

We stand there on the bridge for a time watching the

crew unbatten the last hatch. A shiny Diesel engine pushes a train of cars loaded with iron ore up the long incline and out on the trestle above the ore pockets. Within a few hours the ore will flow into the hold of the *Pontiac* and she will start back for Lake Erie down the route over which she has come. For this routine is repeated over and over again, eight months of the year, from the clearing of the ice in April to the freezing of the channels in December. It is the drama of the movement of ore—as high as 93,000,000 tons in one year during World War II—over the busiest waterway in the world, to add supremacy to the greatness of America.

We bid good-by to the captain and mates and climb the long, long flight of steps to the top of the dock. It is like seeing the city of Marquette from the air. You begin to understand why Doctor Hewitt came to this spot to live nearly a century ago, and why Peter White lived his life here from boyhood on and gave so many benefactions to the town he helped found and foster.

Mr. A. Syverson, general manager of the Lake Superior and Ishpeming Railroad, receives us and invites us to climb into his unique red Packard automobile waiting on the tracks. It is fitted with flanged steel wheels to run back and forth over the railroad. It is fast, comfortable and just a little noisy from the friction of the wheels as it rolls down the long sharp grade from the top of the dock past the sorting yards, and up the slopes to Negaunee. The country is rugged and wild, and the leaves of the second-growth timber are flaming red and gold with the first autumn colors. There are 12 miles of gray protruding rock, of pines and hardwoods, of bridged gorges and tumbling streams. And then we emerge into the somewhat open, rolling area around Negaunee and Ishpeming. Our eye is caught by the dug-out and abandoned open pits, the sunken acres where the earth has settled into old underground mines, and the great shaft houses which dot the landscape. Some of them are old and solidly built like the donjon of an ancient castle. Some are new, and one, on a hill overlooking Teal Lake, is still under construction.

We are immediately struck by the parklike neatness of the whole area around the shaft houses. The lawns are green, rolled and neatly clipped, the walks are bordered with flowers, and the trim buildings are banked with flowers and shrubs. They radiate pride in good house-keeping and devoted husbandry. The houses of the miners, many of whose families have been here for two or three generations, are equally neat and well-tended. It is a gracious place, not a grim and traditional mining town. The digging and handling of ore is inevitably a dirty process in itself, but the company and its men have made and kept their surroundings beautiful where ugliness might so easily have invaded and conquered.

The terrain of this Upper Peninsula iron country is rugged and varied. The rock cliffs jutting out sharply from the hills are gray under the sun. The timber scaffolding of the great ski slide and platform climbs up through a clearing on the hillside, and the waters of Teal

Lake sparkle in the long and handsome basin to the north. Trainloads of ore move out from the various mines to the main tracks that go down to Marquette. There is a special quality in the atmosphere itself, something unique in the sweep of the activity here, something about the place which speaks of history, which unites present and past, and which bears witness to men's hopes and achievements. For we are standing now at the spot where iron ore was first discovered on the Upper Peninsula. In 1845 it was a remote wilderness known only to a tribe of superstitious Chippewa, a few surveyors and a handful of explorers. Today it is one of the great underground iron-ore mining centers of the world. The old abandoned pits above the lake and the tall new shaft house rising on the hill near by mark vividly for us the dramatic development from an exposed vein of ore in a forest to a shaft driven down through the rock into an ore body lying 4,000 feet below the surface.

The spectacle stirs our imagination and sends our thoughts back to the day of the beginnings to follow the story of a century of iron and the men who turned it to our use.

2

DISCOVERIES ON THE MARQUETTE RANGE

A PYRAMID monument of varicolored iron and rock slabs stands at the fork of a road on the outskirts of the city of Negaunee. It bears a tablet with this inscription:

This monument was erected by the Jackson Mining Company* in October 1904, to mark the first discovery of Iron Ore in the Lake Superior region. The exact spot is 300 feet northeasterly from the monument to an iron post. The ore was found under the roots of a fallen pine tree, in June 1845, by Marji-Gesick, a Chief of the Chippewa Tribe of Indians. The land was secured by a mining "permit" and the property subsequently developed by the Jackson Mining Company, organized July 23, 1845.

Two phrases in the inscription awaken the imagination: "first discovery of Iron Ore in the Lake Superior region" and "ore was found under the roots of a fallen pine tree by . . . a Chief of the Chippewa." And we look

---

* Since March 1905, a part of The Cleveland-Cliffs Iron Company.

to the story behind these potent phrases. It begins with
the original land survey field notes in the firm handwrit-
ing of William A. Burt, United States deputy surveyor.
We leaf through to the record for mid-September 1844.
Burt and his party were ranging over this previously unexplored land along the east boundary of Sections 1, 12,
13, and 24 in Township 47 north, Range 27 west—that
is, between Negaunee and Ishpeming (Indian words
meaning the "Lower" and the "Upper"). The weather
had been cloudy and Burt had trouble getting an observation to check his magnetic needle. The needle had
been varying sharply. Here are some of the entries in
the field book:

> North on East Side of Section 24
>
> 2.20 Variation 48° 00′ W.
> 11.70 do 76° 00′ E.
> 29.75 do 20° 15′ E.
> 32.00 do 18° 00′ E.
> 35.00 do 12° 00′ E.
> 48.00 Var. 4° 45′ E.
> 60.00 Var. 0° 00′
> 76.50 Var. 65° 00′ W.
>
> North on East Side of Section 13
>
> 5.50 Variation 65° 45′ W. on top of Ridge
> 77.20 Var. 83° 30′ W.

These entries are followed by a note that "in some places
on North half, the needle would not take any direction
but dip to the bottom of the box." On page 32 in another

note: "Two good solar compasses were used on this T. line & the Variation of the needle determined by both—when the Var. was above 45° or 50° the needle appeared to be weak like one nearly destitute of Magnetism." And appended to the page, apparently in the hand of Douglass Houghton, is the observation: "Spathose & magnetite Iron ores abound on this T. line."

Burt's official diary of 1844 supplements these field observations:

East boundary of Township 47 North, Range 27 West. This line is very extraordinary, on account of the great variations of the needle, and the circumstances attending the survey of it. Commenced in the morning, the 19th of September; weather clear; the variation high and fluctuating, on the first mile, section one. On sections 12 and 13, variations of all kinds, from south 87 degrees east, to north 87 degrees west. In some places the north end of the needle would dip to the bottom of the box, and would not settle anywhere. In other places it would have variations 40, 50, and 60 degrees east, then west variation alternating in the distance of a few chains. Camped on a small stream in section 13.

We especially mark the absence in this record of any excitement in the mind of the great surveyor, any hint that he understood that he was walking over one of the world's great treasure chests of iron ore or any glimmering of the immense wealth that lay buried there under the leaves, the sod and the tree stumps. It was just an immense and remote wilderness that needed surveying, and the solar compass, of which he was the proud inventor, was proving its superiority, as he knew it would, over the unreliable and fluctuating magnetic needle which a woodsman's ax could swing or magnetite ore deflect.

Young Jacob Houghton, brother of Douglass, was barometer man in Burt's party. He was much more expansive. This is his account of the famous September day:

On the morning of the 19th we started, running the line south, between Ranges 26 and 27. So soon as we reached the hill to the south of the Lake, the compass-man began to notice the fluctuation in the variation of the magnetic needle. We were, of course, using the Solar Compass, of which Mr. Burt was the inventor, and I shall never forget the excitement of the old gentleman [he was 52] when viewing the changes of the variation—the needle not actually traversing alike in any two places. He kept changing his position to take observations, all the time saying, "How would they survey this country without my compass? What could be done here without my compass?" It was the full and complete realization of what he had foreseen when struggling through the first stages of his invention. At length the compass-man called for all to "come and see a variation that will beat them all." As we looked at the instrument, to our astonishment the north end of the needle was traversing a few degrees to the south of west. Mr. Burt called out, "Boys, look around and see what you can find!" We all left the line, some going to the east, and some to the west, and all of us returning with specimens of Iron ore, mostly gathered from outcrops. This was along the first mile from

Teal Lake. We carried out all the specimens conveniently.

Perhaps Burt's restraint was only the caution o tist. If he did not realize at the moment what he had stumbled on, a few more months of observation, added to the growing excitement over Douglass Houghton's discoveries in the Copper Country, inspired him to give out a considered statement two years later, 1846. He said:

It may be reasonably inferred that not more than one-seventh of the number of Iron ore beds were seen during the survey of the Township lines; and if this district of Townships be subdivided with care in reference to mines and minerals, six times as many more will probably be found. If this view of the Iron region of the Northern Peninsula of Michigan be correct, it far excels any other portion of the United States in the abundance and good qualities of its Iron ores.

This statement is a tribute to Burt's trained eye and even more to the genius of Douglass Houghton. Both men are among that remarkable but too little-known fellowship of hardy surveyors and scientists whose contributions to the development of this country were of incalculable value. Houghton was a slight, intense man, with keen blue eyes and restless small hands. He was born at Troy, New York, in 1809. He was graduated from the Rensselaer Institute in 1828 with unusual distinction in chemistry and natural history, and almost immediately appointed to teach those subjects in that institution. He went out to Detroit in 1830 on invitation of General Lewis Cass to give some lectures on chemistry and geology. He was not a fluent or graceful lecturer, but his wide knowledge and his general brilliance captivated Detroit. Cass persuaded him to stay. The famous Schoolcraft expedition was about ready to set out on its voyage of discovery to the sources of the Mississippi. Houghton was appointed by the Secretary of War as surgeon and botanist to the expedition. The journey through this little-known region and the association with the scientists in Schoolcraft's party were an admirable training for his later work.

Houghton was appointed geologist for the newly created state of Michigan in 1837. He took particular interest in the wild waste of the Upper Peninsula which was given to Michigan in return for the withdrawal of her claim to the strip of territory including Toledo and what became Lucas County, Ohio, at the mouth of the Maumee River. He immediately organized his department to develop as speedily as possible the hidden resources of the state. He appointed C. C. Douglas and Bela Hubbard as his assistants in mineralogy and geology. They pursued their task with vigor and enthusiasm and published their findings in a series of annual reports, beginning in 1840. The reports of 1841 and 1842 carried a comprehensive and accurate analysis of the potential mineral wealth of the Keweenaw Peninsula—a region heretofore known only through Indian tales of fabulous copper lodes, and from fragmentary observations of travelers.

A financial crisis which gripped the entire country forced the state of Michigan to suspend Houghton's field work, but this did not halt his restless planning. He prepared and read a paper before the geologists in Washington in 1844. He proposed that the linear field surveys of the U. S. public lands be linked with a geological and mineralogical survey of the entire country. The plan caught the attention of the Commissioner of the General Land Office. He recommended it to the Congress and the Congress made an appropriation for the work, to be directed by Houghton.

Houghton re-entered the field with his parties of experts. He combined the line surveys with careful field observations on the geology, flora and topography of the Peninsula. A barometer man was attached to each party to take readings as they went along. These data added a good vertical cross section of the terrain to the usual horizontal line map, and furnished, as Houghton stated in one of his reports, "all that was needed to make a true, complete, and minute exhibit of the topography of the country." In addition to all this, Houghton, who suspected iron ore lay in these hills, had asked for magnetic readings at each compass station. It was the first time that a survey of this kind had been undertaken. Like the Geiger counter locating uranium a century later, the magnetic compass thus detected the iron resources hidden in the hills. The nature of the variations, as indicated in the passage which has been quoted from Burt's field books, was a guide to the horde of explorers who soon entered the region to secure leases.

Houghton lost his life on the night of October 13, 1845, on Lake Superior off Eagle River when his open Mackinaw sailboat capsized in a storm. He was only 36, but he had crowded his few years with immense activity and had made a great contribution to his country. His work was carried on by a surveyor and scientist only a little less gifted than himself. He was William A. Burt.

Burt was born in Massachusetts in 1792, but in the same year his parents took him west to New York State. He had no formal schooling whatever. He learned the art of land surveying and taught himself astronomy at night by the light of a pine torch after the day's work on the farm. When he was 17 his family again migrated, this time to the far west of Erie County, New York. He served in the War of 1812, married, and then worked his way out to St. Louis by surveying farms as he went along. He failed to get a job as government surveyor. He settled in Michigan Territory, where he built mills, practiced surveying and served constructively in the Territorial Council. He worked on his solar compass to free surveying from the vagaries of the magnetic needle. It was a remarkable achievement for a self-taught man. He took his invention before the Franklin Institute at Philadelphia in 1835, and received a medal in commendation. Later, he received from the hand of Prince Albert at the

World's Fair in London (1851) a prize medal for his compass.

It was this compass, used by all the parties in the peninsular surveys, which kept the lines straight through the iron ranges, and led Bela Hubbard to append a tribute in the official report of 1845:

In noticing some of the scientific results of the survey of the past season, the duty would be imperfectly performed, were I to omit calling attention to the unwonted accuracy with which the lines have been run. This accuracy has been attained by the exclusive use, by all the parties, of "Burt's Solar Compass;" an instrument to [sic] well known to need more than a bare allusion, but the great value of which has been more than fully confirmed during the surveys the past season. This remark will seem justified, when it is considered that nearly the whole region of country traversed by these surveys, abounds with mineral attractive to the magnet; that the needle has been almost constantly acted upon by causes which produced deviations from the true meridian of the earth's magnetism, and often so powerfully as to completely reverse the direction of its poles. A variation fluctuating from 6° to 20° on either side of the true meridian, was not uncommon, through the length of an entire township; and it seems difficult to imagine how the lines could have been run with the ordinary surveyor's compass.

Burt received his appointment as U. S. deputy surveyor for the district northwest of the Ohio in 1833. The summer of 1844 found him with his party running the lines on the Marquette Range, enduring all the hardship of long days in the field in all kinds of weather, fighting mosquitoes, pitching camp at the end of the day's run and writing up his notes at night by the light of the camp-fire. Like so many other surveyors, he was content to do his appointed work and make report. He was not an entrepreneur, and neither he nor any of his party ever engaged in the exploitation of his discoveries or reaped any profit from them. For that enterprise a different or-der of genius and hardihood was needed, and there was a plentiful supply of it in expanding America.

Knowledge of the wealth of this region spread more rapidly and more widely throughout the land than is commonly supposed from the popular writings on the subject. Maps based on Houghton's and Burt's work were published and circulated everywhere. The reports were studied. Spirited young American enterprise was stimulated close to fever pitch. Legend, of course, got mixed up with the facts, and Americans began to dream of quick wealth from the copper and silver, perhaps even the gold awaiting them along the south shore of Lake Superior. Jacob Houghton, member of Burt's party which first discovered the iron mountain at Negaunee, published a little book in Buffalo in 1846 on *The Mineral Region of Lake Superior*, complete with the significant reports of Douglass Houghton on the geology and to-pography of the region. He appended a splendid detailed map of the Upper Peninsula, showing its physical fea-

MONUMENT TO AN ERA—BAY FURNACE, 1870-1881

LOADING DOCK IN SCHOONER DAYS, MARQUETTE

Photograph by Henry Mayer

THE MODERN DOCK, MARQUETTE

tures and spotting the mining locations and leases that
had been issued by the Secretary of War up to July 17,
1846. Almost a thousand permits had been granted, and
104 companies had been formed to exploit them. The
permits were heavily concentrated in Detroit, Cleveland,
Pittsburgh, New York and Boston, but they were also
scattered in goodly numbers all over the northern part
of the nation, and into Kentucky, Maryland and Washington, D. C. The list of officers of the companies contains many famous names of the period: Zina Pitcher,
Rufus Choate, Caleb Cushing, August Belmont, Oliver
Newberry.

Most of these people were interested in copper and
silver. But the report for 1845, prepared after Houghton's death by his assistant Bela Hubbard, contained
these two pregnant paragraphs concerning the Negaunee-Ishpeming region:

The largest extent of iron ore noticed, is in town 47
north, range 26 west, near the corner of sections 29, 30,
31, 32 [around Negaunee and south of Teal Lake].
There are here two large beds or hills of ore, made up
almost entirely of granulated, magnetic and specular iron,
with small quantities of spathose and micaceous iron.
The more northerly of these hills extends, in a direction
nearly east and west, for at least one-fourth of a mile, and
has a breadth little less than 1000 feet, the whole of which
forms a single mass of ore, with occasional thin strata of
imperfect chert and jasper, and dips north 10 degrees
east, about 30 degrees. At its southerly outcrop the ore
is exposed in a low cliff, above which the hill rises to the

height of 20 to 30 feet above the country, on the south.
The ore here exhibits a stratified or laminated structure,
and breaks readily into sub-rhomboidal fragments, in
such a manner as will greatly facilitate the operation of
quarrying or mining the ore.

This bed of iron will compare, favorably, both for extent and quality, with any known in our country.

It is hard to determine just how much of a part in
attracting people to the region this accurate scientific
data played in comparison with the wild flying rumors
that spread from town to town and office to office across
the land. Certainly some of the sounder companies engaged outstanding scientists of their own to visit the
region and report; certainly also many others were lured
to the region largely by the color of the rumors of great
wealth to be had for the taking. There was a little of
both in the adventure of Philo M. Everett which led him
to the spot above Teal Lake, where the monument stands,
in the spring of the year 1845.

Everett was one among the thousand who had secured
permits in the Upper Peninsula. Born in Connecticut in
1807, he was now a merchant living in Jackson, Michigan. As the news of the discovery of minerals spread
through the land in the winter of 1844, Everett gathered
a dozen of his neighbors about his stove to talk over the
prospects and to plan a trip to the country in the following spring. They formed themselves into "The Jackson
Mining Company"—an ambitious name for a group of
businessmen who knew little about mining and nothing

about the wilderness where the minerals were presumed
to be deposited. And their first interest was in copper
and possibly silver. Everett became treasurer and exploring agent to go up to find a location. In July 1845 he
set out from Jackson with Frank Carr, Edward Rockwell
and Jed Emmons for the Upper Peninsula. We note the
route: over the new strap-rail steam road to Marshall; by
stagecoach through Battle Creek to Grand Rapids; by
tote wagon, with hard boards laid across the bed for seats,
for four days, to the Straits of Mackinac; by canoe, with
Indians paddling, to Mackinac Island; by the S. S. *General Scott* to the Sault. Here they bought from Indian
boat builders for $45 a 40-foot white cedar Mackinaw
boat with two tamarack masts and split sails. For another
ten dollars they got the boat hauled round the Falls.
They hired Chippewa Chief Madosh, the "Admiral," to
sail the boat up Whitefish Bay, along the south shore of
Lake Superior, past the Pictured Rocks to Grand Island
and on to the mouth of the Carp River at present Marquette. The journey required 21 days, a fact which points
up the extreme isolation of the mineral country in the
mid-1840's.

At this point it is difficult to detach fact from legend
and tradition. Perhaps quick tradition in a case like this
is more accurate than dead fact. Everett had only the
sketchiest knowledge of the region. And he was looking
for copper. At the Sault he met Tipo-Keso (Full Moon),
niece of Chief Marji-Gesick, whose village was on Teal
Lake in the midst of his hunting grounds. She mentioned

the mountain of ore near the lake where great blocks of
heavy rock lay on the open ground, and she gave directions to Everett for reaching the spot by way of the Carp
River. Everett decided to go look at it. He pitched camp
on the shore of Lake Superior at the mouth of the Carp.
With light packs containing tents, blankets and food, he
and his party tramped through the hard-maple forests
along the Indian trail up the rugged gradual slope about
15 miles to the Chippewa camp on Teal Lake. They
were hospitably received by Chief Marji-Gesick who
helped them make camp, entertained them with Indian
dances and smoked a ceremonial pipe with them. The
following day they were taken up the hill to the south.
There, under the roots of a big pine tree, lay exposed
the iron which had excited such awe and superstition
among the Chippewa.

There was one particularly large boulder detached and
lying exposed, which was later sent to the Smithsonian
Institution where it may still be seen. In a sense, this
discovery was the beginning of the city of Negaunee, and
it is appropriate that the center of the city's official seal is
a picture of the stump under which the boulder was
found. Everett and his party explored the vicinity.
Everett concluded that it was "a mountain of solid ore,
150 feet high. The ore looks as bright as a bar of iron
just broken." They made several locations, in accordance
with their permits, including this legended one which
they called by the single stubby name, "Iron." They
carried out a few hundred pounds of specimen ore and

sailed back in the Mackinaw boat, reaching home on October 24.

Everett had thus gone forth to find copper and silver and had returned with samples of iron ore which he had found lying exposed on the ground. He sent some of it over to the ironmasters in Pennsylvania to be tested. Their furnaces and firing methods were not adapted to handling this high-grade Superior ore and they pronounced it a failure.

The Jackson Company was not easily discouraged. Everett's oral report and the exhibit of specimen ore inspired them to send out another expedition to the same location in the following spring, 1846. This time it was headed by Abram V. Berry, president of the company. They made the same hard journey to the Carp and back through the woods to Teal Lake. They re-examined the Iron Mountain and spent twelve days tramping over the hills around Negaunee, exploring further prospects, including near-by Cleveland Mountain. They built a rough log house on the Jackson claim near the pine stump and left some men there to occupy the property. They also dug out a few more hundred pounds of ore, and again returned to Jackson. Berry sent these samples to Mr. Olds of Cucush Prairie, a capable ironmaker who operated a small forge, using local bog ores. He smelted the ore in his blacksmith fire and hammered out a bar of fine metal—the first iron ever made from Lake Superior ore. Everett had one piece of it made into a knife blade. There was no question of the quality of Marquette ore.

The Jackson Company was now convinced that it should exploit iron ore rather than copper, and it proceeded with all haste to get into operation. It did not occur to these men to bring out the raw ore. They thought only of reducing it to blooms at or near the mines. To this end Berry, Everett and their Jackson associates got enough capital together to buy a forge, bellows and all the other necessary machinery. They loaded this equipment aboard ship in 1847, sailed it up to the Sault, portaged it around the Falls and then reshipped it to the mouth of the Carp River. There it was again unloaded and transported up the Carp to the falls of that river about three miles east of the Jackson Mine. They had no sooner got the forge set up in this wilderness than a flash flood roared down the Carp Valley and washed it away. It was rebuilt later in the year and a dam was thrown across the river to provide power to blow the bellows. A dozen men pried loose the ore at the mine and broke it into small chunks. Others cut down the hardwoods near the forge and burned charcoal in crude pits. And, using this primitive method, Ariel N. Barney, an able ironmaker of that day, forged the first iron ever made on Lake Superior on February 10, 1848. It was high-quality iron. It was sold to Captain Eber B. Ward of Detroit, a famous shipbuilder and operator, and one of the early promoters of the Sault Canal. He made it into a walking beam for the steamship *Ocean* where it served sturdily for many years.

The Carp River forge had four fires; each produced a

lump every six hours which was then hammered into blooms two feet long and four inches square. Its daily capacity was from three to six tons, but it seldom produced at that rate and it was idle much of the time. And the blooms that it did produce had to be hauled by sled through the woods to Marquette, there to await the call of a vessel willing to take it on as cargo for the ports below. The operation lost money; but it was the first attempt to make iron on the Upper Peninsula, it proved the fine quality of this vast ore deposit and it publicized the location far and wide.

3

GRAVERAET'S ADVENTURE

WE LEAVE the Jackson men to struggle with their problems while we turn to follow briefly the fortunes of another group which, like the Jackson Company, would become a part of the continuing Cleveland-Cliffs Iron Company. This was the Marquette Iron Company. The mention of the name recalls the warning issued in one of the first reports on this mineral-bearing peninsula issued by Douglass Houghton, a warning that proved in retrospect to be direfully prophetic. We remember that his own journeys, five of them, were along the south Superior shore, and that he had never personally seen the iron-ore deposits which lie seven miles or more inland at the nearest point. He was, therefore, writing about copper and silver when he cautioned speculators that the lure of quick and abundant wealth would "prove the ruin of hundreds of adventurers, who will visit it with expectations never to be realized. The true resources have as yet been little examined and developed, and even under the most favorable circumstances we can-

not expect to see this done but by the most judicious and
economical expenditure of capital, at those points where
the prospects of success are the most favorable. I would
by no means desire to throw obstacles in the way of those
who might wish to engage in the business of mining this
ore, at such time as our government might see fit to permit it, but I would simply caution those persons who
would engage in this business in the hope of accumulating wealth suddenly and without patient industry and
capital, to look closely before this step is taken, which
will most certainly end in disappointment and ruin."

Like so much sound advice, it fell on deaf ears. Companies were formed overnight, claims were secured without definite boundaries and quite without knowledge of
their value, and stock was sold in a wild market. Very
few of the 104 companies as of July 1846 survived or
actually got into operation.

But the story of the iron ore exposed around Teal Lake
had reached the ears of one of the memorable characters
of Michigan and the Upper Peninsula. He was Robert
J. Graveraet, founder of the city of Marquette, one of
the giants of those days, tall, muscular, magnetic, alert
and tireless, a natural leader of men and completely at
home in the wilds. He spoke French and German as well
as several native Indian dialects. He had come out to
the northwestern frontier and was living at Mackinaw
when the news of the discovery of iron ore by Burt's party
filtered to the outside world. Though he had no money
of his own and no financial backing, he determined to

go up to the range and have a firsthand look for himself. He paddled over to Mackinac Island, sailed up to the Sault and then made his way round the shore to the Carp River. He tramped back to the Jackson location, explored the outcropping two miles farther west which became known as the Cleveland Mountain and went on to find and inspect still another deposit known later as the Lake Superior Mine.

Graveraet was immensely excited by all this ore and his ambitions were stirred into grandiose hopes. He then and there envisioned the prospect of making this range in the Upper Peninsula a center of the iron industry which would rival if not surpass the Pittsburgh area in the east. He worked fast. Without worrying about any prior or conflicting claims, he persuaded two men, John H. Mann and Samuel Moody, to try to pre-empt the Cleveland location by building a log cabin on it and holding possession until the Government was ready to sell. They not only built a shelter, but they cleared the ground around it, and planted a garden and protected it with firearms.

In the meantime the indefatigable Graveraet was successful in finding some financial backing for his enterprise. Waterman A. Fisher, a well-to-do cotton millowner of Worcester, Massachusetts, like so many others, had become interested in this mineral region. He sent Dr. Edward Clark as his representative out to the Peninsula to look over the prospects for copper (not iron). At Mackinaw in the summer of 1848 Clark met Graveraet, who painted an alluring picture of the iron-ore deposits only a dozen miles back on the range from a good harbor. He told of the acres of hardwood that would make good charcoal, of the quality of the iron and of the ease with which it could be procured and sailed to market. Clark got excited enough to make the trip with him back to the Carp River to see the location and the Jackson forge in operation. Clark, too, was impressed. He took a sample of the iron from the forge and hurried back to Worcester to report. There to the amazement of Mr. Fisher the sample iron was drawn into high-quality wire.

Graveraet saw in Clark's enthusiasm the possibility of getting financial support in the East. Without waiting for Fisher or Clark to communicate with him, he put on his snowshoes, walked through the snowbound winter wilderness from Marquette to Saginaw and made his way to Worcester to have a personal talk with Fisher. Fisher was captivated by this big, confident man who had appeared out of the wilderness like Elijah the Tishbite before him, and by the prospect of wealth from these iron mountains. He immediately put up the necessary capital against the supposed security of leases to the locations at the Lake Superior and the Cleveland mountains which were being held by Graveraet's men in the log houses with the gardens. He induced A. R. Harlow, a good mechanic, to join them, and to fashion the machinery for a forge.

These men—Graveraet, Fisher, Clark and Harlow—thereupon organized the Marquette Iron Company in March 1849. Harlow began at once to make the ma-

chinery, and Graveraet went back to Mackinac Island to
hire for $12 a month and board nine men and 18-year-
old Peter White, later to become one of the most celebrated figures of the Peninsula and the iron business, to
work for the new company. In April Graveraet took this
little party aboard the side-wheel steamer *Tecumseh* and
sailed through ice-filled channels for the Sault. There
they changed to a Mackinaw boat and fought their way
for eight days by sail, oars, poles and ropes through the
icy Superior waters along the shore to the Carp River.
When they beached their boat and their scant provisions
at this harbor, Marquette consisted of two log houses and
a half-dozen birchbark or cedar Chippewa wigwams.
There were no other white men between them and the
Sault. Marji-Gesick's son-in-law Bawgam, a famous Indian from the Sault, was living in one of the wigwams.
He received the party hospitably and gave them a feast
of wild game, fish and potatoes.

From Marquette the party, heavily loaded with food
and equipment, tramped back through the woods and
underbrush to the log house on the Cleveland location.
They cleared away the brush from the ore outcroppings
and prepared the area for mining. Harlow with his party
and the machinery for the forge arrived by the schooner
Algonquin on June 10, 1849. Graveraet, Peter White
and the others left their work at the mine to go down
to the harbor to welcome them. They found them wet,
tired and miserable, huddled among the trunks and tool
chests, on the forlorn beach outside Marquette, where

they had debarked the night before. The first white woman on the Upper Peninsula was in Harlow's party. They went down to the village, felled trees on the high bank near the shore and made some cabins for shelter. They cleared away enough of the forest to erect a storehouse; they prepared a place for a sawmill, a coal house, and a machine shop, and a site for the forge right on the edge of the bank. A few weeks later the schooner *Fur Trader* arrived from the Sault with the boiler and other machinery and supplies. The boiler was plugged up, dumped into the lake and floated ashore. Later when cattle and horses arrived they were thrown overboard and had to swim ashore.

Restless, eager Robert Graveraet seemed to be everywhere at once. He directed the building of the little village and named it Worcester, in honor of the men who were backing the company, though it was soon changed to Marquette in tribute to that revered missionary explorer. More men were sorely needed for the labor of mining, cutting timber, building a wharf and setting up homes and the forge. Graveraet would disappear into the woods, be gone for weeks and then reappear at Marquette after a trip to Chicago, Milwaukee or some place, with horses, tools, supplies and more settlers and laborers. In anticipation of the forthcoming activity which he planned for Marquette, he set his men to work at once building the first dock in the harbor. They felled trees, rolled and dragged them into the water, piled them one across another and then filled in around them with sand

and gravel. Soon they had a dock ready to receive the
ships. Unfortunately they had much to learn about the
capricious furies of Lake Superior. Shortly after the dock
was finished, the winds swept over the lake, blew up high
waves, and the fruits of all their backbreaking labor were
swept away like driftwood during the night, leaving the
harbor as barren as the day that they had landed. The
schooners had to continue to unload by lighter or by
dumping cargo overboard to be floated in until a new
dock could be built. It was one of many in the long evolution from the loose logs, sand and stone to the towering
solid structures which now dwarf the giant freighters that
tie up alongside to be loaded in a few hours.

The little Marquette Iron Company forge on the edge
of the bay was ready for operation in 1850. But the difficulties were too great even for Graveraet. The ore had
to be hauled down from the mine location 12 miles back
on the range, and there were no roads. They had to wait
for the winter snows and drag it down on sleds. There
was no provender for the animals on the Peninsula. Hay,
corn and oats had to be shipped in at heavy expense from
down the lakes. Hay brought $40 per ton and sometimes
more. Two schooners bringing in the winter supply of
grain at the close of navigation were caught in a December storm at L'Anse and frozen in. The need for the supplies was so desperate that Samuel Moody and James
Broadhurst went overland on snowshoes to the vessels
and cut one of them loose. They got some Indians to cut
a channel out to the open lake, and they sailed it under

iced-over canvas into Marquette, arriving on Christmas Day.

Charcoal was scarce and was produced at great expense of labor in open pits. The operation of the forge was spasmodic. What was worse, the financial result was disastrous. Under these conditions it cost the Marquette Company $200 per ton to make and deliver a ton of iron at Pittsburgh where the market price was only $80 per ton. Mr. Fisher could see no prospect of making a fortune for his company by taking a loss of $120 per ton on the iron it made at Marquette.

Not even Graveraet's force could overcome so formidable an economic barrier. The story of his failure is like that of so many pioneers in the history of American enterprise. He possessed in abundance the qualities of vigor, courage, indomitability and imagination. He drove with irresistible energy to get the location staked out, to induce men to come to this hard wilderness to work, to found Marquette and to bring in equipment for operating the mines and making iron. But he lacked practical experience in the tough competition of this business. He failed to foresee the compulsive economic logic of shipping ore to the mills in the big population centers near the coal fields instead of trying to move the industry to the peninsular mines. And partly because he was on the wrong track, he failed to keep the necessary risk capital flowing in to tide him over the first period of heavy losses. He made a great contribution to the development of the Marquette Range, but he was likewise one of the hundreds of casualties among those who rushed into the wilderness on the heels of the surveyors.

Men of long-range vision, managerial experience and financial acumen were needed to make a success of this hazardous venture. These qualities were supplied by a little group of men from Cleveland, Ohio, whose perseverance was not surpassed by that of Graveraet himself. By the time the Marquette Company was ready to abandon its project, the Cleveland company was far enough along to take over its failing venture and absorb it into a successful organization.

From portrait by Charles Hopkinson

WILLIAM GWINN MATHER

SAMUEL LIVINGSTON MATHER

WILLIAMS LANDING, GRAND ISLAND, YEARS AGO

Photograph by Henry May

THE PRESENT SCENE

4

THE CLEVELAND MEN

THESE Cleveland men had got into the iron-ore business almost as obliquely as the Jackson and the Marquette companies. Cleveland had been rising rapidly since 1833 when the Ohio Canal was opened with this Western Reserve city as its Lake Erie terminus. Able and active men, who had accumulated capital and who foresaw something of the great future in store for the growing country, turned their attention to the Upper Peninsula when the reports of the mineral deposits on Keweenaw Point first reached them. One group formed the Dead River & Ohio Mining Company with W. A. Adair as president, George E. Freeman as secretary and M. L. Hewitt as treasurer. They engaged one of Ohio's most noted scientists of the period, Dr. J. Lang Cassels, to inspect and survey the region and make a report. As A. V. Berry was coming back from his expedition in 1846 with his samples of iron, he had met Doctor Cassels at the Sault. They had a long talk about the minerals and the locations. Berry was deeply impressed by the Cleveland scientist.

And well he might have been, for Cassels belongs in that niche of great pioneering spirits along with Houghton and Burt. Born in Sterling, Scotland, October 15, 1808, he had spent two years at the University of Glasgow before coming to this country at the age of 19 to live with an older brother at Utica, New York, and to teach school there. He soon went on to Fairfield to study at the College of Physicians and Surgeons of the Western District of New York. In those days the study of medicine was also the study of all the sciences. One of his distinguished teachers was Dr. James Hadley (Dartmouth, 1809), professor of chemistry, materia medica and mineralogy, including geology. Another was Asa Gray, a graduate of that college, and America's most renowned botanist of the century. Both took keen interest in Cassels. It is hard to comprehend the versatility of this young scientist. He joined the staff of the medical school at Willoughby, near Cleveland, in 1835, taught midwifery and diseases of women and children, chemistry and other subjects, practiced medicine, and during the summers served as first assistant on the geological survey of New York to explore the mineral resources of the state.

Cassels moved to Cleveland in 1843 to become dean of the new Western Reserve Medical School and to continue his scientific work. He had a chemical laboratory fitted up at his own expense; he had one of the few microscopes in the West, one made at Geneva, New York, in

1837, and the second earliest known microscope of American manufacture. In this laboratory he analyzed specimens of coal from various mines. He established his home on Euclid Avenue near the up-and-coming younger industrialists who had settled there. No doubt they had many conversations with this learned man about the news coming out of the Northwest wilderness concerning the mineral deposits. The use of brass was rapidly increasing, and the demand for copper and zinc to make it was pressing. These men wanted to be sure of the facts before they proceeded, and they persuaded Cassels to make an expedition for them in 1845 to explore the mineral prospects on the upper Mississippi River. And in 1846 he went up again, this time to the Upper Peninsula, to examine the minerals there.

He was, of course, primarily interested in copper. It was on his homeward journey from this trip that he met A. V. Berry of the Jackson Company at the Sault bearing the 300 pounds of ore samples from Iron Mountain in Chief Marji-Gesick's Chippewa hunting domain. Berry may have known in advance of Cassels' imposing reputation. Certainly he was greatly impressed by the personal meeting and by his mission. Cassels told him about the Cleveland men for whom he was exploring, of their financial resources and of their determination to go into the business of mining. Berry thereupon proposed that if Cassels' company would share the expenses of taking over and holding the claims and making roads down to Marquette, he would show him to the iron-ore deposits. Cassels agreed, took Berry's boat, and went back along the south shore of Superior to the Carp River. He inspected the region and was amazed at what he saw both at the Jackson location and at the one about two miles farther on which became known as Cleveland Mountain.

What he saw is best described by Foster and Whitney, U. S. Geologists, in a report to the United States Senate in 1851. The Cleveland location, they wrote, "rises in the form of an elongated knob, or ridge, to the height of 180 feet above the small stream in the valley at its base, and 152 feet above the drift terrace, over which the road passes near its northern slope. Its height above Lake Superior is 1039 feet. . . . This mountain of ore . . . is made up, as far as it is exposed, on its sides, which rise irregularly, and in some places with vertical walls, of alternate bands of pure fine-grained peroxide of iron and of jaspery ore. They are . . . twisted and contorted in every variety of form and outline. . . . The deep-red color of the jaspery portion contrasts admirably with the steel-gray of the less silicious bands; indeed the singular beauty presented to the eye on scraping off the mossy covering of a vertical wall thus decorated by innumerable, fantastically-interwoven stripes of harmonizing and brilliant colors, can hardly be exaggerated.

"The width of this deposit of ore cannot be less, at its base, than 1000 feet, and it may be traced for considerably over a mile in length."

Cassels secured this location by permit and hurried

back to Cleveland to report his findings and give public lectures on this region.

It happened that another able Ohio scientist, Charles Whittlesey of Cleveland, had also been making explorations on the Upper Peninsula since 1845. In 1847 he was employed by the United States Government to continue the surveys. Whittlesey, who had been assistant geologist for Ohio, published papers on the geology and mineral wealth of this region, and gave several public lectures to full houses in Cleveland on this wild country west of the Sault and its potential resources. The same public flocked to hear Doctor Cassels who exhibited specimens of silver and copper ore. He predicted that the iron mountain he had examined contained enough metal to lay a railroad all the way to the Pacific Coast. Some people were incredulous and some skeptical, but a few were convinced and were enthusiastic about the possibilities. It was indeed a period of great popular excitement in Cleveland over railroads and new mining ventures. Two of the new companies sent men and equipment out to the Peninsula to open mines, and they were soon shipping back a trickle of copper in barrels to Cleveland.

In the meantime some of the Cleveland men were following up Cassels' report on the iron ore. W. A. Adair, one of the leading spirits, went out to the iron range, also in 1846, to see it for himself and to help hold possession of the claim in the midst of rising controversy over conflicting permits. He shared the growing enthusiasm over the possibilities of the iron ore. He and ten associates agreed among themselves in April 1847 to form a company to purchase the land around Cleveland Mountain just as soon as the Government offered it for sale. They organized on November 9, 1847, as the Cleveland Iron Company. Eleven men divided shares in the company, and later, through redistribution, four other men were taken in, including Dr. Morgan L. Hewitt, a practicing physician in Cleveland, John Outhwaite, a young chemist from England, and Samuel L. Mather, a young lawyer who had recently arrived in Cleveland.

The first certificate of stock, written on plain note paper, is worth noting. It was issued to George E. Freeman, one of the trustees, and reads as follows:

Cleveland Iron Company.
Certificate No. 1.   Shares 850.

This certifies that George E. Freeman is the proprietor of 850 shares of the capital stock of the Cleveland Iron Company and that the holder is entitled to 850—twenty-three hundredth-parts of the capital stock and profits of said company, according to the articles of agreement and association of said company, made November the 9th., A.D., 1847. The stock of this company is transferable on the books of said company by endorsement on the back hereof and surrender of this certificate, provided all assessments made hereon have been paid.

Given under our hands at Cleveland this 27th day of November, 1847.

GEORGE E. FREEMAN
M. L. WRIGHT   Trustees.
JOHN OUTHWAITE

Like the Jackson and the Marquette companies, the Cleveland Iron Company at the time of its organization apparently had no thought of shipping the iron ore down the lakes to the Ohio and Pennsylvania furnaces. They supposed it would be practical to erect forges near the mines, make the ore into blooms and ship them down to market. Among the old papers of the company is an itemized estimate of the cost of making the blooms at Marquette. By running eight fires 250 days in the year, they expected to get a net profit of $24,500. The dream, of course, was grandiose, and it actually cost many times more to produce and deliver the blooms than the market would bring in return on the Cleveland wharves. But that was yet to be demonstrated in 1848.

The first step, naturally, was to stake out and hold their claim to the Cleveland location until the land could be purchased and the title cleared. The process of clearing and validating conflicting claims to the ore deposits proved tedious and annoying. It brought the Cleveland company into direct conflict with Graveraet and his Worcester associates. The Cleveland company had followed up Cassels' report by sending Lorenzo Dow Burnell to the region in 1846 to stake out a claim for purchase and to erect a house on the property to hold possession. He employed Dr. Edmund C. Rogers to build the house and keep someone on the claim. Doctor Rogers had proceeded to do so, and actually had his cabin erected before Graveraet came. While Doctor Rogers was on a trip to Cleveland in 1847, he left Charles Johnson at the cabin to hold the claim. But Samuel Moody and John Mann, whom Graveraet had persuaded to pre-empt the Cleveland Mountain, allegedly burned down this cabin, built a cabin of their own and tried to take over the claim. When George E. Freeman and John Outhwaite came out for the company in the spring of 1848, they found Moody and Mann in possession. They ordered the intruders to get off the Cleveland premises, but Moody and Mann drew pistols and refused. So Mr. Johnson, for the Cleveland company, waited until June when Moody and Mann were absent, and then rebuilt the log cabin. This one was also burned down, presumably by Moody and Mann.

Conflicts of this kind continued until 1850 when the United States Government announced by Presidential proclamation that it was ready to sell the lands. All interested parties were summoned to appear at the land office at the Sault to prove and validate their claims and receive title. Graveraet was there awaiting the arrival of Moody and Rogers through whom he expected to pre-empt both the Cleveland and the Lake Superior locations. But Mann did not come because he had lost his life in a small open boat, November 1849, in a storm on Lake Superior as he was trying to go from Marquette to the Sault. Moody did not arrive either. He and a companion had left Marquette by boat in ample time, they thought, but they were becalmed on the way and failed to reach the Sault until after the sale. That probably made little difference, despite Graveraet's understandable anger, because the Cleveland company had held continuously to its claim since Cassels' visit in 1846 and was able to document its priority to the satisfaction of the government authorities. The valuable property was formally assigned to the Cleveland Iron Company, after some litigation, on the strength of L. D. Burnell's affidavit—preserved as a stained bit of paper—which read:

Whereas I made a mineral location near Carp River, Lake Superior, in the year 1846, supposed now to be the east half of section 10 and the west half of section 11, Township 47, range 27 and claim a right to buy the same under the mineral law of March, 1847. Now, I hereby authorize M. L. Hewitt, or any such person as he may designate, to pay the money and to take a receipt from the land office in my name, and procure the patent from the government, and the title, when acquired by me, I do agree for a valuable consideration received to my full satisfaction by M. L. Hewitt to convey to the said Hewitt, or such person as he may direct for the benefit of the Cleveland Iron Company. In testimony whereof I have hereunto set my hand and seal this 10th day of July A.D., 1849.

L. D. BURNELL

Graveraet did, however, get for the Marquette Company an undivided half interest in the rich Lake Superior mine. Though some litigation followed, for all practical purposes the title to the properties was now cleared and the Cleveland company could proceed with its plans.

5

PIONEERING DAYS ON THE RANGE

WHILE these explorations and negotiations were going forward, the Cleveland men were also actively attempting to perfect their organization. They sought a charter under the laws of Michigan, and the state legislature granted it on April 2, 1850, by "An Act to incorporate the Cleveland Iron Mining Company of Michigan [No. 294]." It is an interesting document.

The first section of the act reads: *"Be it enacted by the Senate and House of Representatives of the State of Michigan,* That John Outhwaite, M. S. Hewit, C. D. Brayton, and others who shall be appointed [associated] with them, are hereby constituted a body corporate, by the name of the Cleveland Iron Mining Company of Michigan, for the purpose of mining, smelting and manufacturing ores, minerals and metals, in the upper peninsula of Michigan." We observe the emphasis on manufacturing. Its capital stock was set at $100,000, divided into 5,000 shares. It could acquire real estate in the Upper Peninsula not to exceed 640 acres, but none in the Lower Peninsula "except a warehouse, lot and office, and such as may be necessary for smelting purposes." The rest of the 13 sections of the act set forth the details of the organization and the relation of the company to the State of Michigan.

Under this authority, the Cleveland men called a meeting at the old Canal Bank on December 26, 1850, to carry out the provisions of the act and to form the company. They sent out notices to the stockholders for their first meeting on February 10, 1851. They met in Samuel L. Mather's office, adopted bylaws, elected Hewitt president and Mather secretary and issued the first certificate of stock to the new president. When the legislature of Michigan passed its general mining law of 1853, the Cleveland Iron Mining Company was incorporated under the act and its capital stock was increased to $500,-000—20,000 shares at $25 each. The stockholders were then listed as follows:

John Outhwaite	6,812 shares
M. L. Hewitt	1,656 shares
Isaac L. Hewitt	1,656 shares
Benjamin Strickland	1,629 shares
Selah Chamberlain	1,500 shares
Henry F. Brayton	3,462 shares
Samuel L. Mather	3,282 shares
E. M. Clark	3 shares

We observe at once the absence of the name of George E. Freeman who had been so active in the original plans in 1848, trustee of the old Cleveland Iron Company and one of its larger shareholders. Freeman had gone out to Marquette with John Outhwaite in 1848 to look at the property. His expense account has been preserved. He paid $14 for a Mackinaw boat which was destroyed as he tried to take it up the Carp River. He paid three dollars for food to take in with him, and one dollar for an Indian cooking kettle. The rough trip back to the mine, and the thought of all the hard problems that would have to be overcome before the ore in this remote and forsaken spot at the end of the earth could be brought to market discouraged him. It all seemed like a foolhardy venture. He resigned as trustee, and assigned his stock to Brayton, Hewitt and Outhwaite. He also assigned to the company the right and title to his interest in the location, receiving $300 in cash in lieu of a $500 anticipated profit.

Freeman's action following personal inspection of the holding indicates how desolate the prospect looked a hundred years ago. He saw that both the Jackson and the Marquette companies were losing money and that the prospects of ever making a profit were discouraging. He probably knew, too, that the Cleveland company was already negotiating with the Marquette Company to take over its interests. This transaction was completed and the stock actually transferred on May 18, 1853. The Cleveland company thus acquired the forges at Marquette, the mine locations, including the Lake Superior, and other property. It was still thinking of making blooms at the Marquette forges, for it had not at this time occurred to anyone to concentrate on shipping the ore itself, partly because of the tremendous barriers to transportation. We do observe, however, that the first ore to be shipped out from the Peninsula left Marquette on July 7, 1852, just as the Cleveland company was getting ready to take over. There were only six barrels of the ore, but it was the first indication of a shift from making iron where the ore was located to the direct shipping of the ore.

It was at this transition stage that the Cleveland Iron Mining Company sent Mr. Tower Jackson up to Marquette in September 1852 as its first resident mining agent. What he found would have discouraged a weaker soul than he. Jackson had brought with him horses and equipment. He could find no workmen to use them. As usual, the men had wavered as they saw winter coming on. Soon the last vessel would leave Marquette, the lake would freeze over, and they would be left as isolated and remote for six long months as the first French settlers on the rock at Quebec after the last ship had sailed around Isle d'Orléans. There was a mass exodus from the wilderness to the more hospitable country "down below." The people who still remained at the settlement were, he said, "uncertain, independent, dreadfully poor, and constitutionally opposed to work." He could persuade only one man to work on the charcoal kilns. He heard depressing stories of the experiences of the last three years. He heard how B. F. Eaton and his brother Watt of Columbus,

Ohio, had come breezily into the region in the autumn of 1850 to make pig iron on the Jackson forge which they had leased. They brought horses, supplies and equipment along with beginners' confidence. They created quite a stir among the inhabitants facing a hard winter of snowbound isolation. They did survive the winter, but when spring came, they fled the place and never returned. Ben, it was said, went to Australia to get as far away from the place as he could.

Jackson heard about the experience of Mr. Czar Jones of the Jackson Company. The company, not too well financed at best, had lost money steadily since it opened its forge in 1848. When spring came in 1850, Jones found himself owing all his workmen and without funds to pay them. The biting winter of isolation and monotony had put the workmen in a dangerous mood. They were talking about hanging Mr. Jones. He engaged Peter White as a guide and fled over the snows to Escanaba.

These and other grim stories of life on the precarious beach-head outpost could not have been encouraging to Tower Jackson as he surveyed the task before him. Even the elements seemed to oppose him. A few weeks after his arrival a hurricane blew over the Peninsula and the fire in the charcoal pits raced out into the timber and only by heroic measures was the little settlement saved from complete destruction.

Jackson persevered. He managed to get eight sleds operating to haul ore from the Jackson Mine, under a royalty arrangement. There was still no road from the mine to Marquette. During the summer months the miners pried loose the ore in the open pit and dumped it into a stock pile. It was impossible to move it in the summertime down the dozen miles over the rude Indian trail to the bay. They had to wait until the frosts came and the snow fell to provide a surface to support the heavy weight of the ore. Then they loaded some 3,600 pounds of ore on the sled and traversed the tortuous Indian trail through the woods, around the projecting rocks, and down the long slopes to Marquette. It was considered good time indeed for a team and sleigh to make one round trip daily during the winter months. And the entire force was doing well if it brought down a thousand or more tons in a hauling season. That was not a great quantity of ore, and no fortune could ever be built on so tiny a trickle.

One little human episode has been preserved in the records of the time which helps us to glimpse the character of the men who drove the teams. It is a letter written by teamster J. M. Hodgson in March 1853 about his celebrated horse named Doctor. The letter must speak for itself:

The most I have been able to haul at one load is 5600 lbs. of ore. There was a great deal to say at the commencement about the Doctor and running to Jackson and Harlow with tales about him, and all about his being used up before spring because he got a few tons ahead of them. The Doctor was a mighty discussion in the

store and lastly they found proper to get a little medicine
into him which gave him a hard time for about three
weeks but the Doctor is himself again now. I will tell
you he was very fretful at the first and they made Tower
Jackson believe he was going down so fast that he thought
proper to give me a smaller box for my sleigh and limited
me to 3600 lbs. The Doctor is in better order than when
he came here.

There were problems on every hand, but the greatest
of them all, and the key to the ultimate success or failure
of the whole peninsular enterprise, was transportation. It
began at the mines where the ore was wheeled out to the
stock pile. It increased from the stock pile to the forge
and the dock at Marquette. But the difficulties were only
begun. There were no ships designed to haul the product
from Marquette down the lakes. There was also the 19-
foot falls at the Sault where the bulky stuff had to be
unloaded, hauled round the barrier and reloaded. And
again there was the lack of suitable ships for the long
haul down to the Ohio and Pennsylvania markets.

The first gap to be bridged was that from the mines to
the dock. Heman B. Ely went out to the Peninsula to
have a look at the problem. He was immediately convinced that a railroad should be built to transport the
ore. The new iron horses would not require hay at $50
per ton and they could pull a bigger pay load. He worked
out an agreement with the Jackson and the Cleveland
companies. He would build a railroad from the mines to

the lake and they would ship over it all their ore. They would pay a dollar a ton for the first two years, then 50 cents, and finally 35 cents a ton when the annual tonnage should reach 125,000. Ely christened the projected road the Green Bay & Lake Superior Railroad Company.

His plans were bigger than any financial backing he could find. The scheme was sound in the long range. Rails were beginning to spread over the nation. Cleveland itself was in a railroad fever and was laying roads out in all directions. These enterprises had tied up a tremendous amount of capital at the same time that they were creating new and unprecedented demands for more iron. Ely was in the same position as Philo Everett and Robert Graveraet. He was an energetic pioneer who saw what ought to be done, but he was struggling in the morass of raw beginnings which inevitably took their toll. Men with capital still thought of this region as a place remote almost beyond the limits of communication. Returns on investment seemed equally remote.

But Ely did not give up. He got enough money together to send in supplies and men to begin laying out the road up and down those rugged slopes. The going was rough and slow. Things got so tight in 1852 that Ely had to sell some of his provisions to get enough money to leave the Peninsula to go below. During that winter when Tower Jackson was trying to get ore down to Marquette by sleigh, it did not look as though a railroad would ever be built. Jackson, therefore, proposed that the Cleveland company build instead a plank road. Such roads also were very popular in Cleveland and vicinity. Euclid Avenue had got out of the mud by laying planks, and several companies were formed to extend plank roads to neighboring towns. Jackson, partly out of desperation, argued that the sure planks would be better than doubtful rails. He argued by letter to his company in December 1852:

We want a plank road to Cleveland mountain. It would be better than a railroad, for if we had a plank road we could haul the year around and the farmers can haul you all the coal (charcoal) you want which you cannot transport on a railroad. A plank road would build up you a nice town and a railroad will not. One hundred teams which would run daily on a plank road would occupy a good many men and teams and the people would settle here and clear up farms, make coal and haul their product to market, and that would make the country prosperous; but a railroad will fill the pockets of a few eastern men and that would be an end to your business. The only prospect of a railroad in my opinion is that it never will be built. Mr. Ely, the agent, had to sell some of his flour to get money to go down with at $5.50 per barrel when he had just come from below. I think that looks squally.

Just how an enterprise in this condition was to "fill the pockets of a few eastern men" does not appear, but the inconsistency did not seem to worry Mr. Jackson. He was more interested in getting his ore to market. And

since Ely seemed to be making no progress on his railroad, the two companies began jointly to undertake the
laying of the planks.

That was a herculean task in itself. Marquette is half
circled by steep wooded hills and outcropping granite
bluffs. The land rises steadily back to the iron range at
Negaunee. The route of the projected plank road followed roughly present Route 28, being a little to the
south most of the way. There were several steep grades.
The roadway had to be cleared, in some places heavily
graded, logs had to be sawed into planks and the planks
laid on sleepers. They could not get or keep enough men
to do the work. They were threatened with strikes. The
correspondence of the managers on the ground to the
officers in Cleveland is filled with desperate calls for
help. "Send up a few men. Send Germans if you can.
They're easier to manage." Ely also caused them trouble.
He contended that he had an exclusive franchise to build
a road to the mines, and he tried to halt the building of
the plank road by injunctions and lawsuits.

Again these resolute men kept doggedly at their task
through hot summer with its swarms of mosquitoes and
winter with its sub-zero snows. They worked at it through
the summer of 1853 and in the spring of 1854 they managed to employ a hundred men on it. They finally got
it finished in the late fall of 1855. It was extended on
from Negaunee to the Cleveland Mine, and for the first
time in any systematic way the company began to get
ore from its own property instead of taking it on a royalty

basis from the Jackson Mountain. Over this new road they were able to haul carts bearing four tons of ore and making one round trip each day. It was still a pretty crude business. Plank roads were rough, and on the steep grades it was hard to brake and hold back the heavy carts. Too often the carts got out of control and rolled down on the mule teams, crushing or killing the expensive animals. Because of the late opening of the road, they brought down the lakes only 1,449 tons in 1855, but in 1856 they managed to ship 11,297 tons; and that was enough to indicate that there might be a profitable future in the business after all if the companies could keep going awhile longer.

The demands on the resident managers were heavy. In June 1853 Tower Jackson was succeeded as mining agent by J. J. St. Clair, a vigorous man with an analytical mind. He saw that it would never be practicable to make iron in quantity on the Peninsula. Since all provisions had to be shipped in, living was excessively expensive. They were shut in and cut off from the outside world for six months of the year. They had to endure "a thousand inconveniences." There was no coal, and the day would soon come when the timber would be gone and charcoal impossible or costly to get. Prepare to ship ore down to the furnaces, he advised; bend every effort toward building the road, constructing docks and developing shipping. He did ship four tons of ore to Cincinnati, via Cleveland, to be tested by Mr. Benton, who had patented a process for making blooms with hard coal instead of charcoal or coke. The tests were successful and created excitement among the members of the company. He shipped another 152 tons to the Pennsylvania furnaces in September, 100 tons in October, another 100 in November, and had left on the docks another 150 tons when the navigation season closed. He proposed to make this ore into blooms at the Marquette furnace during the winter; however, the forge and machine shop burned, and the company decided not to rebuild them, thereby committing itself to developing the facilities for shipping ore. As we read the correspondence of St. Clair to the offices in Cleveland, our eye falls on a note that Philo M. Everett, the pioneer for the Jackson Company, was engaged to quarry ore during the winter of 1853 for the Cleveland company.

6

PRELIMINARIES AND IMPROVEMENTS

AT THIS point Dr. Morgan L. Hewitt decided to go up to Marquette to live. He did not go as a direct supervisor of company affairs. After serving as president for four years, he refused re-election in 1855 in favor of Selah Chamberlain. The company continued to have capable mining agents who looked after the expanding enterprise. St. Clair was succeeded by the energetic William Ferguson and he, in turn, by Arad Kent and Robert Nelson. These men really did the tremendous job of bringing the mine into profit-making production during the decade from 1855 to 1865. But Hewitt's presence at Marquette and his continued active interest in the company played a vital role in its success. The minutes of the directors' meetings show that he came back frequently to Cleveland to take counsel with his colleagues.

As we have already noted, Hewitt was one of the founders of the Cleveland Iron Company and a moving spirit in its development. In those days he used to gather his Cleveland friends around him in his garden to have scientific talks about the discoveries in the Upper Peninsula. For he was another of those early scientists who took all learning as their province. Born at Hartford, New York, on January 20, 1807, he had grown up around Plattsburg, and always remembered the famous battle on Lake Champlain in his boyhood. He studied medicine at Castleton, Vermont, being graduated in 1832. The following year he went out to Cleveland to live and practice medicine. That, too, was a venture, for the little town on the Cuyahoga had only about 2,500 inhabitants; but the canal had just opened, and the population had increased by more than 2,000 in the last ten years. He was very successful. He headed the new Marine Hospital out on Lake Street. He was a leader among the early group of medical men who gathered in and around Cleveland, and actively studied and wrote to improve medical science. It was this interest, apparently, which first brought him and Doctor Cassels together and led them on to the exploration of the Michigan minerals. Both Samuel L. Mather and William J. Gordon were especial friends of Hewitt. Burnell designated him to purchase the claim to Cleveland Mountain at the land office at the Sault, and it was Hewitt who got the office moved from the Sault to Marquette in 1855. He pushed the project to build the road from the mines down to Marquette. He was one of the active spirits behind the building of the canal at the Sault. He made personal

visits to the forges and furnaces around Pittsburgh to tell
the iron men about Lake Superior ore, to encourage them
to experiment and to sell them supplies.

Despite all this evidence of interest, we naturally wonder why this thin, wiry, vigorous and kindly man took
his wife, Sarah Bradley Hitchcock of Cheshire, Connecticut, and his two daughters from their fine home and
friends in Cleveland to this remote frontier a century
ago. There were still only a few houses clinging to the
shelf above the beach and under the circling hills at Marquette. There was only a handful of miners living in log
cabins at the mines in Negaunee and Ishpeming. Life
was raw and restricted and during the winter desperately
isolated. The whole enterprise, after nearly a decade of
struggle, was still something of a gamble.

But Hewitt had made several trips to Marquette and
he was captivated by the natural beauty of the region
which has won the hearts of so many residents during
the succeeding years: the quick burst of spring when
the snows melt and run down through the gorges of the
Carp and the Dead rivers, the delicate shades of green
as the hardwoods come into leaf among the pines, the
bright autumn days followed by crisp starlit nights, the
woods screaming with color, the fishing camps and hunting lodges, and the first winter snowfalls. It has always
attracted strong men of colorful character and developed
the solid human traits of warm sympathies and neigh-
borliness.

The ultimate reason, however, was Mrs. Hewitt. She

loved the region for itself, and besides, being a victim of hay fever, she found on one of her trips with her husband that the malady which tormented her in Cleveland completely disappeared while she was at Marquette. She needed no persuasion from Doctor Hewitt.

Hewitt arrived in 1857 and remained at Marquette until his death in 1889. He not only saw tremendous changes in the Peninsula during those 30 years reflecting the equally unprecedented developments in the nation as a whole, but he was personally responsible for a part of a great many of them.

There were several big jobs to get done. The old plank road was outdated before it went into service. It proved as inadequate in the hills back of Marquette as it did between Cleveland and its neighboring villages. They fastened wooden rails to the plank road and covered them with a thin strap of iron for the cars to run on. They called it the Iron Mountain Railway Company. The strap rails increased the tonnage that could be hauled down and also increased the accident rate. But teams were not the answer. A steam road was needed.

Heman B. Ely, who had struggled so hard for so long against so many obstacles, had finally got his troubles under control. Following the completion of the Sault Canal in 1855, in which he had taken an active part, he had acquired enough capital to operate with, and now, encouraged by the demands of both the Jackson and the Cleveland companies, was about to bring his railway, on iron T rails, to Negaunee and Ishpeming. His road was,

somewhat confusingly, called the Iron Mountain Railroad Company. Thanks to the help of Peter White in
the Michigan legislature, he had received a railroad land
grant that had helped him along. Though he died before
his venture was complete, Ely's brother Samuel carried
on, and the road was ready for operation in September
1857. It was a day of celebration at Marquette when the
little brig *Columbia* sailed into Iron Bay bearing the fine
locomotive named *Sebastopol*—it was a glistening 25-
ton machine made in New Jersey and had cost $11,000.
Her trial run back to the mines was a complete success.
On this road they could bring down 1,200 tons daily. The
engine and cars ran smoothly over the rails, and the *Lake
Superior Journal* proudly announced that "there are now
twelve sail vessels and one propeller loading and waiting
to load with ore," at Marquette.

At the same time the Marquette paper ran an adver-
tisement proving that a new era for the ore business had
now dawned. "Mules and horses for sale," it said. "A
rare opportunity is offered for obtaining large well trained
Mules of the right age for profit and long service. They
are now in good keeping in this city, where they may be
seen. The Cleveland Iron Mining Co., having dispensed
with the use of teams, will sell this stock (nineteen Mules
and also three horses) at very reasonable prices. If not
sold soon they may be sent south where their value is well
understood. H. B. Tuttle, secretary, Oviatt's block." In-
cidentally, their true value apparently was not appreciated
in Marquette, for they were shipped down to Cleveland,

where the company received this communication from the master of the vessel which carried them:

Sir: In making contract with Mr. Kent for the freight on the mules we agreed to take down the men free of charge who were to care for them and prevent their damaging the boat. But they have kicked and churned up our joiner work and stanchions and everything within reach of their hind legs. I don't think $50 is too much to repair the damage.

Docks at Marquette were just as important as the railroad. We have noted how the first crude dock, made of logs, sand and gravel, was washed away by the waves of Lake Superior. Other and better ones met the same fate. The big new dock made by the Sharon Company was broken up and scattered all over the bay by a disastrous storm. The Cleveland company profited by these experiences. The first docks had been little more than a projection of the shore out into the harbor alongside which vessels could tie up. Sweating, hardhanded workmen pushed the ore in wheelbarrows out on this dock. It was then wheeled aboard the schooners. It was a slow, laborious and expensive process.

The Cleveland company built the first semblance of a modern dock. On the site of the old Marquette dock, they built a series of cribs, 20 feet square, out into the lake. They were solid and substantial affairs, filled with heavy stone, and able to resist the angriest waves battering against them. They extended 400 feet into the bay.

On top of this dock they constructed a trestle 22 feet wide and 25 feet high and placed on it a track for the ore cars. The trestle sloped gently toward the bay in order that the cars might be run out under their own momentum. Under the trestle was a series of pockets slanting out over the hatches of the vessels moored to the dock. The ore was dumped into these pockets, and the mouths of the pockets were opened by means of a chain and pulley, allowing the ore to flow through (with a little help) directly into the vessel. Each pocket held about 50 tons, though a few were specially built to hold 80 tons to flow into wheelbarrows to be taken aboard the steamships that would carry the ore. Three schooners and a steamer could tie up and load simultaneously. The dock was ready for operation June 22, 1859, and the honor of being the first ship to load went to the schooner *J. W. Sargent.*

While the problems of land transportation and loading were being worked out, a project of still greater magnitude and ultimate importance was being undertaken at the Sault. Getting around the barrier of the Falls in the St. Marys River seemed the key to the whole transportation problem of the upper lakes.

The site was historic and legended. It had always been a favorite spot among the Indians. Its natural setting was magnificent, it was the center of good hunting grounds, the fishing at the Falls was unrivaled anywhere on the lakes, and its strategic position on the waterway made it the control point for Whitefish Bay and Lake Superior. Nicollet found an old and well-established village there when he first set eyes on it in 1634—over two hundred years before Burt's compass responded to the magnetic ore around Teal Lake. The portage around the Falls was well worn by generations of moccasined feet. When the French took control, they built a fort to command the entrance to the western trapping region and to keep the English traders out. The British later took this over, along with the fur trade, and the North West Company in 1797 built a serviceable little canal with one lock on the Canadian side capable of letting boats loaded with fur through the rapids and a nine-foot lock. They were pulled along by oxen. American troops under Major Holmes destroyed this canal and lock in 1814 and burned the settlement. The canal was rebuilt in 1816, and the settlement slowly grew back. Over on the Michigan side the American Fur Company built a horsecar tramway in 1823 to portage goods around the Falls.

During the decade which we have been describing Sault Ste. Marie became a rough, overcrowded outpost as prospectors, speculators, miners and adventurers poured in following the news of the discovery of minerals on the Upper Peninsula. Beyond the Sault, at the time Burt and Houghton made their discoveries, there were only two little trading posts—one at L'Anse and one at La Pointe.

The young state of Michigan had long been alert to the need of a canal to stimulate the million-dollar fisheries that could be tapped on Lake Superior. It had not yet dreamed of copper and iron ore. It actually got a survey made, plans drawn and a contract let for construction in 1839. But when the workmen attempted to start digging on the government reservation through which the canal had to pass they were met by United States troops and driven off the premises. Michigan spent the next several years trying to persuade the Government to permit construction and to help out on the expense. They failed, largely because of the opposition of the great Henry Clay, who, in arguing against the measure before the Congress, made his famous remark "that it contemplated a work beyond the remotest settlement in the United States, if not in the moon."

That was in 1842. It took ten years of unremitting effort, long visits to Washington, briefs, arguments and supporting data, lobbying and personal pressures by Michigan men and all concerned to get the Congress to change its mind and pass the required legislation. The act was approved on August 21, 1852. It required that the canal be not less than 100 feet wide and 12 feet deep, with two locks not less than 250 feet long and 60 feet wide. It granted 750,000 acres of land to Michigan to help pay for the construction, and it required that the work be started by 1855 and completed within ten years. Authorization from the Michigan legislature was passed in February 1853, and the way was cleared for construction.

The labors of many men had gone into the realization of this dream: the officers of the iron companies; the leading citizens of Michigan and some from Ohio, Pennsylvania and New York; Captain Eber B. Ward, largest shipowner on the lakes at the time; Heman B. Ely; Peter White of Marquette. But the most daring enterprise of all was exhibited by Charles T. Harvey, a resourceful 24-year-old salesman for the Fairbanks Scale Company who happened to be at the Sault at that time recovering from an attack of typhoid fever. He was the western district manager for the company. As the speculators poured in or passed through he felt the general contagious excitement at the Sault. He made a few inspection trips himself and picked out some highly profitable lands for his company from among the acreages donated by the Government for the building of the canal. He was so enthusiastic about the canal that he was able to sell the project to his company. Joseph P. Fairbanks, Erastus Corning, August Belmont and other Eastern capitalists formed the St. Mary's Falls Ship Canal Company and undertook the herculean task of building the canal.

Young Harvey was general agent. He had made full recovery from his illness—in fact, he was the most energetic man in the whole Peninsula and he lived on into his eighties to see his prophecies more than realized. He gathered up labor from all over the country and even met the immigrant ships at the seaboard ports to lure hardy workers away from the competing railroad agents. At one time he had as many as 2,000 workmen at the Sault, digging, blasting, wheeling, hauling, laying stone and carving out the canal around the Falls. They worked through the hot summer and through the cold short winter days when the thermometer sometimes fell to 35 degrees below zero. Cholera broke out in 1854, mowing down nearly 200 men; but they were buried quietly at night and those who escaped worked on under the determined and driving force of Harvey without interruption to the lengthening ditch and the rising walls of the two locks. All supplies and equipment had to be shipped in by boat, most of them over the thousand miles of Great Lakes and connecting rivers.

The canal was finished in less than two years. On April 19, 1855, Harvey himself opened the sluice gate to let in the waters of Lake Superior. And on June 18 the canal was ready for use. There was, of course, a ceremonial opening befitting such an historical achievement. Representatives of the Government, federal and state, officials from the companies, public-spirited citizens, came to the celebration. On that day the first ships locked through, the *Illinois* going up and the *Baltimore* going down. And just two months after the opening the two-masted schooner *Columbia* passed down carrying on her deck the first shipment of iron ore through the Sault. Her cargo was 120 tons of Marquette ore consigned to the Cleveland Iron Mining Company and bound for the Crawford and Price wharf in the Cuyahoga River, "unless otherwise ordered by W. J. Gordon, of Cleveland, Ohio," as the bill of lading noted. Four days later the schooner *George Washington* sailed from Marquette with the second shipment of 322 tons to the same destination. The Cleveland Iron Mining Company sent down

1,447 tons that season. This flow of ore would soon make it evident that the canal at the Sault, costing just under a million dollars, was one of the best investments ever made in the future of America.

The effect of the opening of the Sault on the iron industry and transportation was little short of revolutionary. It was immediately reflected in the size of the upper lake fleet. Several vessels had been built at the Sault. In the early days they were very small schooners, like the *Mink*, a red cedar bottom of only 40 tons, built in 1816, which was later taken through the rapids and placed in service between Detroit and Buffalo. Early in 1845, when the news of the mineral discoveries began to spread, there were only three schooners on Lake Superior operating out from the Sault. Seven more were added to the fleet that same season by hauling them at great labor around the Falls and refloating them on the upper level of the St. Marys River. These included the *Napoleon, Swallow, Chippewa* and *Fur Trader*, which carried men and supplies to the settlement at Marquette. And in that same year the propeller *Independence* was hauled up on rollers to become the first steamboat on Lake Superior. The next year, the demand still growing, the *Julia Palmer* was converted from sail to steam with side wheels and hauled over the Falls. This side-wheeler apparently could not cope with the seas of Lake Superior; at any rate she was lost the following year on the Canadian shore. The *Manhattan* was hauled up over the Falls in 1849, the *Monticello* in 1850 (lost the same year), the *Baltimore* in

1851, the *Peninsula* in 1852 and the *Sam Ward* in 1853.

This was about the extent of the Superior fleet before the opening of the canal. The little ships had to carry whatever tonnage could be brought out of Marquette. The captains did not like ore as cargo, because the ships were not made for it. The *Baltimore*, the first one down through the canal, was built as a stylish passenger boat. It was the only one operating on a schedule. It met Colonel Sheldon McKnight's other Pioneer Line ships sailing, also on schedule, between Detroit and the Sault. Obviously the captain and the crew did not want dirty ore piled on the deck. It soiled and disfigured the ship, reddened the hands of the crew and left stains that were hard to wash off the deck. The blooms were less objectionable, but these were unprofitable in the market. But now, with a free waterway from the loading docks to the receiving ports on Lake Erie, and with a growing demand for ore, the shipowners saw a profitable business ahead and the need for vessels adapted to the new cargo. We shall soon see the rapid evolution of the ore boats, but we note now the first response to the combination of a shipway and a rising market for all the ore the northern range could produce and deliver.

There was a remarkable change at Negaunee. In 1855 when the canal was opened there were only six rough-hewn log houses in the little settlement back there at the pit among the gray, glacier-scoured rock ridges around Teal Lake. Only about a dozen men worked at the mine, prying loose ore, carting it to the stock pile and loading it on the sleighs. It was a bare holding operation, a kind of tenuous beachhead on the edge of an unconquered wilderness. Negaunee was an outpost of Marquette on the bay, dependent on that little seaport village for communications and supplies. And Marquette itself was only a cluster of houses hugging the water front. Its population was about 200. It seemed to center around the forge, the new loading docks sticking out into the bay and the railroad struggling back up the escarpment to find its way west to the mines. Marquette now took a new lease on life, built some more houses, brought in more people and incorporated as a village in 1859. By 1859 Negaunee had jumped to more than 300 workers. Two miles to the west at the Cleveland Mine some log houses were going up, and Ishpeming had its beginning in 1856. The reason for this spurt of growth after nearly ten years of slow and doubtful struggle was the interlinking combination of a growing need for iron, the opening of the Great Lakes waterway through the Sault and the operation of the railroad from Marquette to the mines.

A few bare statistics tell the story. Up to 1855 it is estimated that about 25,000 tons of ore had been taken from the Jackson Mine and around 5,000 from the Cleveland. About 7,000 tons were taken out of these mines in 1856, and over 25,000 tons in 1857. That was a panic year, and the depressed economy was reflected in the output for 1858—22,876 tons. But in 1859 it rose to 68,832, and in 1860 it boomed to 114,401 tons, about a fourth of the output coming from the newly opened Lake Superior Mine in the same vicinity.

Moreover this increasing volume flowing directly to Lake Erie ports without interruption of costly rehandling at the Sault was immediately reflected in the cost of shipment. In 1855 it was costing the operators $3.00 per ton to get their ore from the mines to Marquette, and $5.00 more to get it from Marquette to the Lake Erie ports. Only 1,447 tons were shipped down that year. But in 1856, when 11,297 tons passed through the Sault, the cost had dropped to $1.27 from Negaunee to Marquette, and $3.00 from there to the southern lake ports. In 1857 when 26,184 tons went through the locks, the cost from the mines to the loading docks was the same, but the rate from Marquette to the lower ports dropped to $2.67 per ton. And in 1858, with 31,035 tons locking through, the rate from Negaunee to Marquette had again gone down, to 87 cents per ton, and on the lakes to $2.09. The increased volume, coupled with the new transportation system and loading techniques, had thus made it possible to get ore from the mines to the Lake Erie ports at a rate lower than the cost of sending it 12 miles from the range to the Marquette dock just three seasons earlier.

The most obstinate barrier to success was thereby broken through, and the iron-ore industry of the Upper Peninsula seemed at last to be firmly established and the bright future so long dreamed of and planned for about to be realized.

7

SOME EARLY DIRECTORS

THE secret of the Cleveland Iron Mining Company's success lay in the nature and the quality of the men who took the responsibility for investigating, organizing, planning and carrying out against heavy odds this pioneering venture. A serious mistake in judgment would have brought failure. Any slackening of energy or loss of vision and confidence in the dark moments would likewise have lost the venture. They never faltered. We have already glimpsed the character and work of M. L. Hewitt. His brother Isaac L. was also a wise director of the company during these formative years from 1852 to 1862. He owned the profitable forwarding and commission business in Cleveland at 81 River Street where John D. Rockefeller workēd as a young man.

Selah Chamberlain was a newcomer to Cleveland. Born in Vermont in 1814, he had had a wide experience in canal and railroad building. In 1849 he came out to Ohio to build the Cleveland and Pittsburgh Railroad. There he became a friend and next-door neighbor of

Samuel L. Mather. He got interested in the mining company and was elected to its board of directors in 1854, serving until his death in 1891.

With the completion of the Sault Canal and the new prospects which that opened up, the directors persuaded W. J. Gordon to assume the presidency. No happier choice of leadership for this next period could have been made. He had come to Cleveland in 1839 when he was 21 years old and that booming port center of the Western Reserve and terminus of the Ohio-Erie Canal was luring so many young men with its opportunities. Gordon chose the lucrative business of commission merchant and wholesale groceries. He prospered and carefully invested his capital in many enterprises. Though he was not one of the original organizers of the Cleveland company he knew intimately the group of young men who had incorporated it, and he was keenly interested in the venture. He investigated the prospects for success, felt assured and became a stockholder in the company in 1853. With characteristic energy he went out in August 1854 for his first visit to Marquette. In a letter dated August 22 he communicated his impressions to his friend Samuel L. Mather:

I visited the iron mountain week before last and have examined our property generally and am entirely satisfied with my investment. It does not vary much from my expectations as my sources of information before coming here were reliable and intelligent. Yet the mind can scarcely realize the wonderful deposit of iron in our hills without the aid of actual personal observation, it being almost incredible.

From that point on Gordon was one of the most active members of the company. He became a director on March 5, 1855, and served in that capacity for 26 years. He was the president of the Cleveland Iron Mining Company for ten years, from the opening of the canal through the Civil War period—1856 to 1866.

These first three presidents made a great contribution to the growth of the industry, but the central directing personality was Samuel Livingston Mather. He helped organize the company, he was for 40 years its leading director, for 14 years its treasurer and for more than 20 years (1869—1890) its president. And when he left office he was succeeded by his son William Gwinn Mather, who served until 1933, then became chairman of the Board of Directors, in 1947 honorary chairman, and in 1950, at the age of 92, was still appearing regularly at his office in the Union Commerce Building. It is a remarkable fact that the active interest of these Mather men, father and son, spans the full century of iron and the entire history of the Cleveland-Cliffs Iron Company through all of its combinations.

Samuel L. Mather belonged to the celebrated New England family which has woven its name into American cultural history. He was born in Middletown, Connecticut, July 1, 1817. He attended the newly opened college in his home town, being graduated from Wesleyan in its first class of 1835. Then he entered business with his father in Middletown. Later he moved on to New York City. He found time to make two voyages to Europe which broadened his outlook and set the pattern which his sons would follow in their time. He came out to Cleveland in 1843 at the age of 26 in order to look after his father's extensive real-estate holdings in the Western Reserve of Connecticut. There he found himself among the group of brilliant young doctors, lawyers and commission merchants who had settled in the rising city. He studied law and was admitted to the bar. From the outset he was a civic leader. It was in his office that the first plans were laid for the organization of the Society for Savings.

Mather was among the first to be attracted by the reports of mineral discoveries in the Upper Peninsula. He was the one who interested Cleveland capital in what was still a mere speculation. In retrospect his colleagues credited him with paving the way and laying the foundations for making Cleveland the great controlling center of the iron industry which it is today. He was an unusual combination of venture and caution, having the faculty of being able to calculate the risks, offset them against the opportunities and make decisions accordingly. And when he was convinced of the balance, he moved with driving force. He seems never to have wavered in his conviction that someday the source of raw material for industrial America would be the shore of Lake Superior. Despite the long years of constant outgo of capital, he was sure of eventual success. The wreckage of hundreds of speculative hopes did not discourage him. Failure was the natural and inevitable result of get-rich-quick schemes unsupported by sound financing and orderly, realistic planning. Mather brought both into his own company. He never crushed or took advantage of others who fell by the way when the going got hard, but dealt honestly and justly in all his company organizations according to his firm New England code.

It is important to keep this personality in mind as we follow the developments of the epic of iron. Few companies have succeeded in overcoming the many discouraging problems and transitions which have faced the iron-ore business through all the years of its life and survived for a century.

One episode in the management of the company in its early years illustrates the kind of crises it faced and the ingenuity of the directors.

The financial problems were serious in those days when the banking system was still fragile and recurring panics afflicted the nation. The Cleveland Iron Mining Company had been capitalized in 1850 at $100,000 in stock. This was increased to $500,000 in the reorganization of 1853. The directors had to levy periodic assessments on the shareholders to keep the company going. Some of them, of course, grew fainthearted and objected. As late as 1857, when an assessment of one dollar per share was levied, one of the shareholders wrote Mr. Mather that he could not respond to this call. "Put my name down as in favor of selling out the whole thing, paying the debts and dividing the balance among stockholders."

This note reflected the prevailing bleak mood of despair that came upon the country with the sharp and disastrous Panic of 1857, which took a heavy toll of business. But Mather, Gordon and their associates did not share the defeatism, though they were fully aware of their extremity. They had labored for seven years to get operations going at the mines and ore flowing south to the furnaces. The season of 1856 indicated that victory was within their grasp. But now the Panic threatened to collapse the whole operation. The market for ore disappeared. The mills around Pittsburgh were all closed. Distress spread on the Marquette Range. William Ferguson, the mining agent at Marquette, persuaded the men to stay on and work, waiting for their pay until the ore could be sold. The company, facing a need of $50,000 or more of currency at Marquette alone for the year's operation, had to find more working capital or perish.

Mather went to New York and Boston bankers to borrow money on the note of the company. His personal integrity and the previous history of the company were in such high standing that a few of the banks did grant loans. They were too small, however, to meet the heavy demands. Gordon had gone out to Marquette for a personal view of the problems at the mines. After looking over the situation, he and Mather devised the system of "Iron Money" to carry them through the crisis. It was a simple device for keeping exchange flowing during the time of shortage and stringency. They issued small drafts ($5, $10, $20 and $50), nicely engraved, printed and numbered, and drawn on the treasurer in Cleveland or the financial agent in New York or Boston. These were sent up to the range where they substituted for regular currency. They were circulated, given and received with the same confidence as though they had been bank notes. Three or four months or more would elapse before they were presented to the banks for redemption. It was by such planning and careful management that the company was brought through the crises and into the era of productivity and profit. And on March 1, 1882, the capital stock was increased from $500,000 to $2,500,000.

It wasn't easy, however, for the men up at the mines and at Marquette to have an understanding of the problems faced by the company down below or to have any realization of what goes into the organization, planning and financing of a new and venturesome industry. In fact there is no indication that they had any real interest in it. They were the floating labor of the day—immigrants who had just arrived on these shores, French and Canadians who were at home in the woods and moved on from one lumber outfit to another, and Germans, Irish, and Cornishmen who were attracted by the promise of higher pay. They were not concerned with the cost of producing ore, of forging blooms, of building railroads and docks, of launching and chartering ships, of testing the ore in the furnaces and of selling ore to a skeptical market. This was all the somewhat private business responsibility of those few men who hoped to develop an industry. The men were thinking about the quality and the adequacy of the food and shelter and the regularity of their pay. If a ship bearing money for the pay roll failed to make its schedule, as sometimes happened, the men were ready to rebel without further inquiry. If anything went wrong, if the food got short, or other cause for discontent arose, they might strike, or they might board a boat and sail away or don snowshoes and take off across the Peninsula for ports below.

8

INTO PRODUCTION

ONE whole decade had now gone by—ten years of struggle, of trial and error, of financial outlay and discouragement, of small successes and large failures. The prophecy of Douglass Houghton that many would rush in without proper thought, and that few would survive the wave of speculation, had come sorrowfully to pass. There would still be other failures in the future, but the close of the first decade found the Cleveland Iron Mining Company on the threshhold of achievement.

The iron mountains west of Marquette now began to present a scene of accelerating activity. Instead of an unknown region remote as the moon, two little villages were growing up near the mines and Marquette was a port of call. Passenger steamers from the lower cities ran excursions to the Sault and cruises around Lake Superior. The harbor at Marquette and the open-pit mines at Negaunee and Ishpeming were almost as exciting to the travelers as the Pictured Rocks of *Hiawatha* fame along the shore east of Grand Island and present Munising.

The mineral deposits were taking on national significance. For, by 1859, iron ore was really rolling down over the new railroad. There were 68,832 tons that year, nearly a fourth of it from the Cleveland Mine.

The work at the mines was still a simple job of manual labor. When you stand now at the edge of one of the old pits and survey the immense activity on the surface of this region and consider the miles of underground tunnels, equipped with millions of dollars' worth of intricate machinery, your mind is taxed to flash back to this scene a hundred years ago. A few dozen men worked from the floor of the open pit which looked more like a quarry of reddish rock than a vast iron mine. They hammered drills down through the rock with sledge hammers. They blasted loose the face of the wall. They picked away at the chunks, sledged them into proper size and loaded them into a two-wheeled dumpcart. The cart was drawn by a horse or a mule over the short distance from the face of the wall to the tiny tramcars waiting on the track. These cars were then pulled out of the mine by a primitive engine, which may still be seen on display at Ishpeming, and hauled down the escarpment by the puffing locomotive *Sebastopol* or by its fellow called *C. Donkersley*, named for the first superintendent of the railroad, which had begun its daily round trip from mine to dock and back in 1858.

The men had to work hard during the open season between frosts. For in those first years, when the heavy snows fell, the engines had to stop operations because the tracks could not be cleared and the trains could not get through. Even at best these first engines could haul up the steep grade only ten empty cars. But this small burden was such an advance over the old sleigh and plank-road eras that it seemed revolutionary. Except for minor improvements and the employment of more men to get the ore loose, this primitive process of mining carried through the Civil War years and into the Reconstruction period.

Again the tonnage figures succinctly and dramatically tell the story of more men coming in, of better transportation and of growing demand, and of the opening of new mines on the range:

	Tons
1862	124,169
1863	203,055
1864	247,059
1865	193,758
1866	296,713
1867	465,504
1868	510,505
1869	649,097
1870	856,245
1871	818,966
1872	949,073
1873	1,174,972

When the Civil War began there were three mines of all the companies in operation: Cleveland, Jackson and

Lake Superior. The New York, the Marquette and the Lake Angeline went into production in 1864; the Humbolt and Iron Mountain were added in 1865; the Edwards and the New England in 1866; three more were opened in 1868; and in 1873, when the year's production exceeded a million tons for the first time, the ore was coming out of 40 pits carved into the ore bodies in and around the Negaunee-Ishpeming region.

Down below, the furnacemen, after much experimentation, had learned how to make the finest and strongest iron out of Upper Peninsula ore. The armies of the North carried guns and dragged up to the battle lines cumbersome cannon, many of which were cast from this supply. The rails spanning out into a network across the Northern states were fashioned from Marquette iron. The blockade of the Mississippi had detoured traffic through the North and revealed to shippers the economy of the route across the Great Lakes or along their shores. It was one of those timely interlockings of events which have so frequently in our history given a new impetus to growth just at the moment when the upward curve seemed to be leveling off.

The expanding activity in the Upper Peninsula was not limited to the mining and shipping of the ore. One secret of the success of the Cleveland company was its sagacious interest in developing by-products or intimately allied enterprises. One of these was the combination of lumber, charcoal and furnaces which developed as a necessary and natural adjunct to the mining of ore. The

Photograph by Lake Shore Engineering Co.

SPECIAL UNDERGROUND MINING OF CLIFFS SHAFT LUMP ORE

TRAMMING, CLIFFS SHAFT

Photographs by Lake Shore Engineering Co.

DUMPING, CLIFFS SHAFT

forges had already demonstrated their failure by the time the Cleveland company got under way. Like the first furnaces, they made "little iron and no money." So the company from the outset of actual production concentrated on mining, shipping and selling the raw ore. The forge which they acquired when they took over the Marquette Company was, as we have noted, soon abandoned.

But no company could hope to survive and grow without an adequate reserve supply of potential ore-bearing land. Real estate and mines were inseparable. The company soon found itself the holder of large blocks of real estate and impelled to acquire more as time went on. It had to have land in Marquette for its offices, warehouses, docks and approaches. It had to have a right of way back to the mines, and it had to have a big supply of timber, first for the plank road and the dock, then as a protection against the possibility that charcoal might be needed if the Peninsula did get into the busines of making iron at the mines, and ultimately it would need millions of cords for timbering the drifts as the surface ore gave out and the mines went underground. So after the early law was modified, the company got heavily into the lumber and forestry industry.

The minutes of the directors' meetings through these early years are filled with the record of buying and selling real estate on the Peninsula. The need grew year by year, decade by decade, until the company holdings reached to a million acres, and a separate Land Department was organized in the 1890's to give expert management to them.

The plan to make the Upper Peninsula the center of the iron industry died hard. In theory the concept seemed logical. It was a simple carry-over from the charcoal era in Pennsylvania and Ohio. A man built a furnace near a supply of bog iron and hardwood, hired a few skilled men and started making iron. Scores of learned articles were written to prove that this same combination would work up here. The ore was abundant, the hardwood forests appeared to be inexhaustible, fluxing rock was near by; why not build furnaces, reduce the ore and ship the compact product down to the manufacturing plants? The suggestion was so appealing that a total of 25 furnaces were erected in the vicinity. Most of them failed. The early ones were simple affairs. As in the Ohio and Pennsylvania region, you come unexpectedly upon their relics as you wander about the countryside. The heavy stone foundation walls and stacks, usually built against the side of a hill, are still in place, with the brush crowding in on them and covering the old charcoal pits. There were ten of them in Marquette County at the outbreak of the Civil War. And while the war urgency lasted and the hardwood near the furnaces held out some of them were successful.

The first blast furnace on the Upper Peninsula was the Pioneer at Negaunee, built by the Pioneer Iron Company. Charles T. Harvey of Sault Canal fame was the moving spirit in the Pioneer Company, which he and Edward T. Hungerford incorporated in 1857. These two men went to East Stockbridge, Massachusetts, to inspect the furnaces there and to get L. D. Harvey, a practical furnaceman, to build one or two for them in the Marquette district.

They told L. D. Harvey of the richness of this ore—65 per cent and over—of their contract for a supply, already broken for the furnace, at a dollar per ton of iron made, and of the birch and maple timber ready for making charcoal. Harvey agreed to go out and erect two stacks of ten tons each. He went to Detroit with 22 men and their families on May 20, 1857, and then sailed north on the wood-burning steamer *General Taylor*. They ran into ice on Whitefish Bay and were blocked for one whole night by an ice field at Grand Island. On June 3 they got to Marquette—the first and the last trip, Mr. Harvey said, he ever took on a steamboat.

Harvey went by plank road and mule team back to Negaunee the following day. He explored the district and found a perfect location for the furnace on the north side of Partridge Creek opposite the Lucy Hill ore bed. A little distance away was a ledge of rock, 15 to 20 feet high, where he could get the stone for the walls and stack. A train of mule carts rumbled out from Marquette with supplies and with lumber from the sawmill, and within a few days' time there was another cluster of cabins in a clearing at Negaunee. The men blasted stone, erected derricks to handle the blocks and built the foundations for the furnace.

The steam railroad got through to Negaunee in Au-

gust, and its first shipment was five carloads of brick for
the Pioneer furnace. Then it brought up the engine,
boilers, blowers, hot blast and pipes which had been made
in the East and shipped to Marquette. One has great
admiration for the skill of these practical furnacemen
building in the wilderness, far from a machine shop, and
overcoming formidable obstacles at every turn. There
was a five-foot snow that winter. In April 1858, nonetheless, the structure was complete, the furnace fired and
in due course Harvey cast the first five pigs of iron made
in the region. The second furnace was blown in the
following spring.

The glowing prospectus of Harvey's company which
proposed a realizable profit of $18.25 a ton was shattered
by the facts. By September 1859, the paid-in capital was
$125,000, the floating debt was $95,000 and for some
time the company lost money on every ton of ore it
smelted. But the furnace did survive its early losses and
became an important part of the growth and economic
life of Negaunee. The town was thrown into a "panic"
when the Pioneer burned down in 1874. It represented
half of Negaunee's industry at the time, and the citizens
thought this catastrophe was the end of everything. But
the furnace was rebuilt in 1877, and operated continuously until 1893 when it was acquired by The Cleveland-
Cliffs Iron Company. By that time it was obsolete. The
two old stone stacks were inefficient and were wasting
precious wood by-products. The Pioneer was abandoned

in 1893 and its place was taken by a new charcoal furnace and chemical plant at Gladstone, Michigan, seven miles north of Escanaba. The remains of the old Pioneer landmark may still be seen at Negaunee.

Other furnaces were built and blown in during the 1860's and 1870's. Most of them used charcoal, but a few were designed to use anthracite coal. With minor exceptions, the story of one was the story of them all. There are no reliable figures on the actual production of these Upper Peninsula furnaces, but a fair estimate indicates that they had produced over 1,500,000 tons by the close of the nineteenth century. The Pioneer furnaces had accounted for well over a third of this output.

In the total production of ore from these mines and iron for the nation this tonnage is not significant, but a few men by skillful management laid the basis for their fortunes by this manufacture of pig iron. One of them was Peter White, whose name has frequently entered these pages. White was only 18 years of age when he first came to the site of Marquette with Graveraet's company in the early spring of 1849. He had been on his own since he was 14 and had maintained himself by keeping store at the Mackinac Island trading post, by clerking in a Detroit store and doing such odd jobs as he could find. He shipped on the lakes, and was at the Sault during the first excitement over the discovery of copper. He eagerly joined the party to go out to Marquette to build a forge and open a mine. There, driving oxen, felling trees and helping build the first cabins on the site, he grew big and powerful. When a shipload of Germans arrived ill with fever, Peter White carried water from the lake to bathe them and he nursed them back to health. He operated the general trading post for the Marquette Company. In the company of Indian friends, whose dialects he learned to speak, he made journeys on snowshoes from the isolated village to the lake ports to get mail, and by his own shrewdness he caused the Government to establish a post office at Marquette.

After the Marquette Company sold out to the Cleveland Iron Company, Peter opened his own store. He soon added to it an insurance and real-estate business and later on a bank of which he became president. President Buchanan appointed him Register of the Land Office and Collector of the Port of Marquette. W. J. Gordon met him, paid tribute to his abilities, and sought his advice on various business matters affecting the growth of the company's interests. White at one time looked after the vast real-estate holdings of the Cleveland Iron Mining Company; he married Dr. M. L. Hewitt's charming daughter Ellen. Serving several terms in the legislature at Lansing, he was personally responsible for much of the legislation to promote the Upper Peninsula, and he helped persuade the Government to grant lands to aid in the building of railroads to tap the mineral deposits. He went to Washington to press the Congress to build the Sault Canal, and he had the satisfaction of playing a prominent role at the semicentennial celebration of the completion of that vital project. He saved his own bank and other enterprises in the Peninsula from ruin in the days of the issue of "Iron Money." The Federal Government in 1864 levied a tax of 10 per cent on the use of this kind of paper money. Since Peter White's own bank had paid out through use and renewed use of these issues over a million dollars, his tax alone would have been ruinous. A total of $10,000,000 was due the Government under the Treasury estimate. White got through the Congress a bill for relief from this oppression and probably saved the companies from bankruptcy.

Peter White had an interest in the Bancroft Furnace, built by Stephen R. Gay in 1860. Before the Civil War had created unprecedented demands for iron, the furnace failed financially and White had to take over as secretary and treasurer of the company. He sold pig iron to the captains who were willing to take it on consignment to the lower pots. A considerable quantity of this iron had piled up on the wharves and was lying there when the war broke out. White knew that this iron would soon be needed. He sailed down from Marquette, buying back his iron at the ports as he went along. Then he went on to Cleveland and Pittsburgh where he sold a thousand tons in a single day and made a profit of $35,000 in two weeks. The best grade of Bancroft furnace iron sold for $95 a ton that year, the highest price ever paid. The furnace was saved and the iron business at Marquette was given a boost which carried it steadily forward through the ensuing years.

The furnaces which produced this iron ate up charcoal by the thousands of bushels and the charcoal pits consumed the forests by the thousands of acres. In the year 1869, when the Pioneer furnace produced 9,500 tons of iron, it used the timber from 1,500 acres of land around Negaunee-Ishpeming. One acre would produce about 35 cords of wood which in turn would smelt 14 tons of iron. Somewhere near 330,000 acres were cut over during the first half century. By 1903, when charcoal elsewhere was being displaced by coke, the furnaces of the Upper Peninsula were consuming the forests from 10,000 acres of woodland each year, an average of 30 acres every day of the year.

This sounds like a formidable inroad upon natural resources, and it was. But before we lament we must remember that this timber was put to good use to convert ore into iron, while in other regions where the stand was equally good it was hewed down, piled up and wastefully burned solely to clear the land for farming. French Canadian woodsmen were paid good wages to lumber in the forests. As the forests were cut away on the iron range, new deposits of ore were discovered and opened up. The clearings encouraged the towns to plant gardens and keep cows on the grazing land. A few farmers settled there to raise hay, potatoes, sheep and swine to supply the hungry local market that had been completely dependent upon expensive imports from below. Others took up land farther away and made cash returns by clearing their forests and selling their wood or their labor to the companies.

All in all the lumbering and charcoal aspects of the mining industry were a large-scale activity. The first charcoal was burned in crude pits. Then ovens of stone, lined with firebrick, were built in a row against a slope. Others were made of stone in the shape of beehives, some were square brick kilns holding 80 cords of wood, and a few were built of cast iron protected inside by firebrick. The blue smoke from these burning charcoal kilns rose in a score of places in the Marquette district. Back in the woods the lumberjacks, organized into crews, swung axes, pushed and pulled crosscut saws and reduced the hardwood trees to cord wood.

Oxen, mules and horses, and then small wood-burning steam engines hauled the wood to the kilns. Some of the finer logs were sent to the new sawmills that were springing up in the district where they were fashioned into lumber, sash and doors to build houses for the increasing population. Marquette had 1,000 people by 1860 and 4,000 in 1870. Negaunee was having a corresponding growth and Ishpeming was beginning to expand. The sawmills could hardly keep up with the demand. The *Lake Superior Journal* of May 17, 1856, announced that at Marquette "the various public improvements are being carried forward as fast as men and materials for building can be obtained. There is at present a lack of sawed lumber, not owing to a scarcity of timber, but to the want of a sufficient number of mills for sawing it up. There are two churches in process of erection. . . . Everyone is busy in erecting fences, laying plank sidewalks, and other work calculated to improve the general appearance of the town."

More men came to work in the lumber camps and the sawmills. The forests fell rapidly before their industry. When one tract was cut over, the crews moved on back to the next one. They cleared a road for the wagons, or laid track for the tramways, built a new logging camp to eat and sleep in, and kept the cordwood and logs rolling in to the furnaces and the sawmills. Not until near the close of the century did the more careful planners begin to avoid the waste and build plants to utilize the valuable by-products of the wood. This utilization would become a major industry and a direct outgrowth of the mining operations. So, too, would the vast program of reforestation and controlled cutting sponsored by The Cleveland-Cliffs Company.

Peter White did not live to see more than the beginnings of this new era. He died suddenly while pursuing his vigorous way at Detroit on June 6, 1908, as he neared the age of 78. He had long before become the outstanding personality on the Peninsula, its best-loved citizen and the living symbol of its astonishing development. He was the most notable host of upper Michigan, known far and wide for his genial hospitality at his town house and at his hunting lodge deep in the woods. His memory is still green almost half a century after his death, and his philanthropies, like the fine Peter White Library, the statue of Père Marquette and the Presque Isle Park still contribute to the civic life of the town he loved. A Cleveland-Cliffs freighter sails the lakes bearing his name on her sides.

9

DOCKS AND FREIGHTERS

THE miners, many of them Cornishmen who had come up from the bog-iron and charcoal pits of Ohio and Pennsylvania, were blasting, picking and sledging iron ore from ten mines on the Marquette Range in 1867. They had brought the production from 1,449 in the canal year of 1855 up to 473,567 tons. This output was collected on the tracks of the Iron Mountain Railroad and hauled down to the docks at Marquette. For this city on the protected bay was, and continued until 1876 to be, the only shipping port for Lake Superior iron ore. The volume was so great that it overran the capacity of the lake ships to transport it to the waiting furnaces below.

The pace had been rapid since the *Columbia*, trim-looking with her white-banded sides, broke out an American flag from the yardarm of her mainmast and sailed for the Sault with that first little cargo of iron to pass through the new locks. The tonnage kept on mounting, but the company was still dependent on the caprice of the captains to get its cargo aboard the ships as wild tonnage.

106

The shipowners were very independent and even a little scornful of the ore business. When W. J. Gordon tried to make a season contract with the Western Transportation Company of Chicago in 1856, he got this curt answer: "We think we would not contract to carry any specified amount of iron ore for your company or make a price at which we would carry ore, preferring to take the going rates of freight and more or less ore as may suit."

The following year Gordon was successful in letting two contracts with shipowners. Samuel S. Burt agreed to call regularly at Marquette for ore in return for preference over other carriers who might decide to take on a load when convenient to them. He would deliver the cargo "in a substantial and insurable vessel, by steam or otherwise" to the Lake Erie ports as directed for three dollars per ton of 2,240 pounds. Loading and unloading expenses would be shared equally by the owner and the shipper. The company would also favor Burt's ships with any upbound cargo under its control at the current rates. Gordon also that year made a similar charter with Captain Alva Bradley, of Vermilion, Ohio, a shipbuilder and one of the biggest and most influential owners on the lakes. And the next year Bradley launched a brand-new fleet of schooners and brigs to carry ore. With the aid of these carriers the enhanced tonnage flowed down the lakes and tortuous connecting river channels to market.

The scene at the loading dock and the receiving wharves was turbulent and roisterous. Until the first pockets were built, the loading was all done by hand.

Hundreds of strong arms and backs were needed to push
the wheelbarrows laden with ore onto the decks or dump
them into the holds. More men, stripped to the waist and
grimed with sweat and red ore dust, labored in the hold
with shovels to trim the ship by moving the ore forward
aft and to the sides. An expert boss-trimmer on deck with
a plumb bob and measuring line directed their work. For
these light wooden sailing ships had to be well balanced
to weather the 800-mile journey over this difficult route
without listing, shipping seas or hampering speed. At
the wharves below other groups of men shoveled the ore
from the hold to the deck, shoveled it again into wheel
barrows and wheeled it down the gangplank to the stock
pile.

This whole slow and cumbersome process was an effective challenge to all concerned. And from that day to
this, ingenious men, working to improve it, have brought
it to a miracle of efficiency and perfection. By substi-
tuting loading chutes for wheelbarrows, they solved at
one bold step the problem of getting ore into the ships,
though the trimmers still worked in the hold below and
kept watch for heavy chunks that might punch holes in
the bottom or sides. At the Lake Erie ports they first
replaced shovels with a tub or barrel and a rig of block
and tackle, and let a horse lift the ore up out of the ship.
Then they installed an engine to do the work of the horse.

As the tonnage continued to mount, the ships which
had been designed for other cargo had to be modified
and the company had to enter the transport business to

guarantee deliveries. The story of the evolution of these lake freighters is one of the most fascinating in the annals of transportation in America. By 1867 it was becoming obvious even to the most reluctant shipowner that the great cargoes of the future would be ore and grain coming down and coal going up the lakes. The handsome schooners were good fast ships for passengers and package freight, but, even with the best designs, the masts, booms and sailing gear usurped valuable space for pay loads and interfered with efficient loading of bulk cargo. Three or four hundred tons were their top capacity, and it took a lot of round trips for them to deliver much ore to the furnaces. Steam tugs would tow several of them at a time through the St. Marys, the St. Clair and the Detroit rivers to speed them more safely on their way. Shipyards around the lakes began to launch more and bigger vessels up to the structural limit of wood and sails.

Captain Bradley kept adding to his fleet. He launched the *London* in 1858, and followed it soon afterward with the *Exchange* and the *Wagstaff*, which sailed ore for the next 25 years. In the single year 1873 he launched six more; and then, seeing that the days of sails were numbered, he began to build steamships. The Cleveland company took the first step toward acquiring its own ships in 1867 when it bought a half interest in the bark *George Sherman* for the sum of $14,000. She could carry 550 tons of ore at a trip. Two years later a Cleveland yard built the first ship designed expressly for the ore trade. She was christened *R. J. Hackett*. She was in principle the forerunner of the characteristic freighters on the lakes today. Her pilothouse was forward, her engines were placed aft, her 'tween deck was free of gear and her hatches were unobstructed and spaced for easy handling of cargo. She was 211 feet long and could carry 1,200 tons. The next year she began towing a consort of similar design. These ships all carried auxiliary sails to supplement the steam engines.

In 1872, when the volume of ore from the range had mounted to 949,073 tons, the leading stockholders of the Cleveland Iron Mining Company acquired a controlling interest in a fleet of steamers and schooners built and operated for the ore trade by the Cleveland Transportation Company. The ships bore famous place names; the steamers were the *Geneva*, the *Vienna*, the *Sparta* and the *Havana*, and the schooners the *Genoa*, the *Verona*, the *Helena* and the *Sumatra*. They were all built at Cleveland except the *Sumatra*, which was launched at Lorain. They carried about 1,000 tons each at $3.50 per ton to the Cleveland wharves.

The coming of the iron age had turned designers' minds to the idea of building ships of metal. The famous old navy ship *Michigan*, with a hull of iron, went into service on Lake Erie in 1843, and she was able to sail the lake in 1913 on the centennial of Perry's victory in the Battle of Lake Erie. Nineteen years later, in 1862, the *Merchant*, the first merchant ship of iron to appear on the lakes, sailed from the Buffalo yards and entered successful service. She was followed by the *Philadelphia* in 1868. These ships were proving the practicability of iron just at the time when the Anchor Line was preparing to enlarge its fleet. In the winter of 1870-1871 it built in its Buffalo yards three new 325-foot steamers known at the time as "the big iron boats." The iron for the ships was rolled at Philadelphia. They were given the names of *China, India* and *Japan*, and they were popular boats on the lakes for the next 30 years. The cost of the boats was $180,000 each. They could carry 150 passengers and 1,200 tons of cargo on 12-foot draft. Their capacity was 1,400 tons, but they were limited by the depth of the shallow channel across the St. Clair Flats.

The captain of the *Japan* was a 26-year-old Scot who was to become one of the great names on the lakes. He was Alexander McDougall, born in Scotland in 1845, the year of Everett's discovery of ore. His family had come over to Collingwood on Georgian Bay when Alexander was nine. He shipped as a deckhand on the *Edith* when he was 16, moved up during the next ten years as porter, second mate, mate and pilot, to become master of the *Japan* in 1871. He helped build the ships, thereby laying the foundation for his later career as the most resourceful designer of his day. He carried wheat, which began to roll down to Duluth from Minnesota's Red River Valley that season, and he brought down iron ore from Marquette. All season long navigation was hazardous because the heavy smoke from the burning forests lay like fog over the lakes. Along with scores of other ship captains he got frozen in at the Sault in 1872. The following spring he and 200 other men sailed back to the mouth of the St. Marys and walked 70 miles on the ice up to the Sault to begin the new season.

The ships were already growing too big for the bottlenecks in the passageways. The St. Clair Flats were deepened in 1872. McDougall, who by this time knew every rock and every twist and turn along the route, personally set up buoys and markers to guide ships past the dangers in the Flats. Harvey's locks at the Sault were also being outgrown, and plans were drawn to build the big new Weitzel Lock, 515 feet long, 80 feet wide and 16 feet deep. It was completed and opened to traffic in 1884. The first iron freighter, as opposed to passenger steamers, was the 287-foot *Onoko*, launched at Cleveland in 1882. And in 1884 came the 310-foot *Spokane*, constructed of steel. The race for bigger ships and more tonnage was now on with a new material which could stand the strain of almost indefinite expansion.

The Cleveland Iron Mining Company watched all these tremendous developments. At a meeting in the autumn of 1888, the directors decided to build two steel freighters to carry their ore. "As long as we deliver so much ore at Lake Erie ports it is certainly very advisable that the company should be able to control the cost of all such ore delivered and not be at the mercy of varying lake freights which would vary the cost of the ore." That year 5,046,503 tons had been shipped down from Lake Superior. These two steel ships were the *Pontiac* and the *Frontenac*. They were the Leviathans of their day, costing around $400,000 each, boasting the unprecedented capacity of 2,500 to 2,800 tons and sailing at increased speed which in turn meant more trips and more pay loads. They were very profitable carriers. The average freight rate from Marquette to Lake Erie ports dropped to $1.22 per ton.

Cleveland company stockholders also acquired the new wooden steamer *Kaliyuga* and the schooner *Fontana* by purchasing a controlling interest in the St. Clair Steamship Company.

By this time McDougall had gained a wealth of experience sailing on the lakes and handling the bulk cargoes. He had carried up to the Lake Superior ports the heavy machinery and iron rails demanded by the iron mining industry and had developed techniques for getting them off the boats with the use of the crew and gangs of laborers. He had studied designs for ships that would more satisfactorily meet the needs of the ore trade. He made models by the dozens, and finally came out with his famous rounded-deck whalebacks with double bottoms for safety against damage to the plates by torrents of ore chunks charging from the dock pockets down into the hold.

Through Colgate Hoyt he got Rockefeller backing for the American Steel Barge Company. He sent 30 barges and steamers down the ways from his Duluth yards from 1889 to 1893. With a crew of 2,000 men he built ten steel ships at once, launching one every Saturday for eight weeks, and two on the ninth. His first barge took

on 1,200 tons of ore without trimming, and was towed
to Cleveland. No. 101, as she was called, was still hauling cargo on Lake Michigan nearly a half century later.
When some of the old masters saw the first of these odd
monsters of the sea, they said, "You call that damn thing
a boat? Why, it looks more like a pig." These "pigs"
became a characteristic sight as they sailed back and
forth during the next decades with their huge cargoes out
of Lake Superior.

The growing ships again got too big for the locks at
the Sault. The new Poe Lock was opened in 1896—800
feet long, 100 feet wide and 22 feet deep. The connecting river channels were dredged to greater depths. In
1897 leading interests in Cleveland-Cliffs organized the
Presque Isle Transportation Company. They ordered
from the Lorain yards of the Cleveland Ship Building
Company a new giant 426-foot steel ship, the *Cadillac*,
with an 18-foot draft and a pay-load capacity of 6,000
tons. She was joined by the *Choctaw*, the *Andaste*, the
Centurion, the *Presque Isle*, and in 1899 by the 435-foot
Angeline to make a fleet of around 45,000 tons as the
first half century ended.

The technique of unloading had kept pace with this
evolution of the carriers. The engine with block and
tackle did away with shoveling the ore out of the ship by
hand, but men with wheelbarrows still had to push it
over the gangplank to a stock pile. Alexander Brown
remedied this. He belonged to a family which has for
almost a full century made significant contributions to

the iron and shipping industry. His father was Fayette
Brown, who came to Cleveland in 1851 to enter the banking business. He visited Marquette in 1857 and was intrigued by the prospects that were unfolding there. As
soon as he had finished his service in the Civil War, he
returned to the Upper Peninsula as general agent and
manager for the Jackson Iron Company, which obtained
its ore from the Jackson Iron Mining Company. He
helped locate the Munising Railroad and promote this
town facing Grand Island as a furnace and shipping port
for iron and lumber. Then, turning to shipping, he had
a fleet of carriers constructed for the lake trade. One of
his sons, Harvey H., after learning the iron business as a
company agent, went into lake shipping with the Northwestern Transportation Company. He was an experi-
menter, and he had ships built of transitional design with
iron sides and wooden bottoms. The first one was appropriately named for his father the *Fayette Brown*.

Alexander, the other son, gifted in invention, became
a bridge builder. After studying the plodding and costly
process of getting ore out of the ship, he devised the
simple solution of movable towers with arms extended
over the ship, rigged with wire cable to convey the bucket
from hold to the waiting car or the stock pile in one operation. Hoover and Mason then invented the automatic
clamshell grab bucket, and the combination became the
famous Brown Hoist. Men were freed from heavy, backbreaking toil, the price of handling ore was again reduced
and the carriers could unload, turn around and sail back

up the lakes without the long and expensive delays at the wharves.

Equally important developments were going forward at the mines. As the timber was cleared away, geologists continued their painstaking survey and exploration of the ore deposits. They were able to trace the outline of the iron formation with remarkable accuracy. They found it to be 35 miles long from the east side of Negaunee almost due west in a canoelike basin to within a few miles of L'Anse, and from three to seven miles wide. Recent drillings indicate that in places it runs down to a depth of 4,000 or more feet. The Huronian rocks in which the ore occurs have been folded and sharply tilted from their original positions by terrific pressures. Eruptive rocks have been forced through these strata. They assisted in the concentration of the ore and protected it from the tremendous pressures and grindings of the glacial invasions. The ore is found generally in separated pockets, not in veins like coal or clay. The hard ores, first to be mined on the range, are found at or near the top of the iron formation. They were concentrated near the old land surfaces and then folded in the geological upheaval of the region. The soft ores are found in the vicinity of Ishpeming lying on top of the intrusive igneous rocks or diorite sheet just below the hard-ore horizon, and in the lower 300 feet of the iron formation in a series of faulted segments or minor folds in the main basin from Negaunee to North Lake.

Each of these pockets became a new "location" and

each location a mine. The countryside was dotted with them. A few miners came in, built a cluster of houses near the opening or pit and founded another village. It generally took the name of the mine and there were 55 mines by 1878; some of them were small and quickly exhausted, but others like the Cleveland, Jackson, Lake Superior, Humboldt, Lake Angeline, Champion, Republic and Michigamme were heavy producers. Champion rose to become a town of 2,500 people, but sank back to its present 300 when the mine was abandoned in 1910 after producing four and a half million tons of ore. Michigamme followed the same cycle, but Republic is still active. These place names on a map outline fairly accurately the lines of the iron range. In the motorcar age the population tends to concentrate in the few large towns, or at Ishpeming and Negaunee. But in the 1860's and 1870's the communities were separated from one another by the cutover forests, each more or less self-contained within its own clearing. By 1870 there were 6,103 people living in the communities around the mines in Ishpeming, 3,254 gathered about the locations in Negaunee and 4,617 at Marquette. Nearly two-thirds of the men at the mines were Irish and Cornish, a tenth were American and Canadian and the rest were from Germany and the Scandinavian countries. Common labor received $1.80 a day, miners around $2.12. It cost $2.64 to mine a ton of ore, and a total cost of $3.50 a ton to place it aboard the cars for shipment.

They were still mining the easily accessible ore in open

pits, and these pits continued to be the chief source of supply through the 1870's and well into the beginning of the 1880's. The sand and boulders were stripped off from the surface above the iron-ore bodies and moved out of the way. Miners then hammered two-inch holes down through the ore to a depth of 15 to 22 feet, tamped in a charge of black powder (they began to use nitroglycerin in 1873) and blasted the deposit loose from the cliff wall. Some of the pockets could be fully exploited in this manner. Others could not. They sloped downward and the formations were quite irregular. The overburden was too thick to be peeled off without excessive cost. The operation began to drive tentatively underground. At first, as at the Jackson Mine, it became an underground quarry or operation in a cave. The miners simply left the overburden and drove under the capping, following the ore. They built incline skiproads back to the wall to hoist the ore out into the open to the cars. If there was danger of the roof caving in, they supported it by leaving pillars of ore under it. Later they drove down shafts to open up ore bodies revealed by test drillings. And by the 1880's, through these successive and experimental stages, the great shaft-mine era was launched on its spectacular career on the Marquette Range.

The transition coincided with the arrival on the scene of a new force in the iron-mining industry in the person of William Gwinn Mather, son of the great Samuel Livingston Mather who had brought the Cleveland enterprise to solid success.

10

RECONSTRUCTION ERA BOOM

Samuel L. Mather had not taken over the presidency until 1869, but he had been giving active direction to the company since its inception. He had kept it alive in the dark days when everything was going out, nothing was coming in and some of the stockholders were giving up in despair. He had never lost confidence or wavered in his optimism over the future of the iron-ore business. His spirit of assurance was so contagious that when the men from the Upper Peninsula came down to see him with gloomy reports of the formidable obstacles confronting them, Mather would draw on his vision of what was to come, would show them that problems were made to be solved and disappeared with the solution, and would send them back to the Peninsula heartened and ready for the next step. He communicated the vision to his son and endowed him with a goodly portion of his own ability and tenacity.

William Gwinn Mather was the second of his two sons, the child of his second wife, Elizabeth Lucy Gwinn

of Batavia, N. Y. He was born in Cleveland, September
22, 1857. He went back for his education to Connecticut
where four generations had lived at Lyme and two at
Middletown. From Cheshire Academy he went on to be
graduated from Trinity College at Hartford in 1877. In
keeping with family tradition he sailed for a tour of
Europe, as he was frequently to do throughout much of
his life, and then began his work with the Cleveland Iron
Mining Company as a clerk in 1878. He became vice-
president in 1885. His father died in 1890. The following
year the company merged with the Iron Cliffs Company
and took its present name of The Cleveland-Cliffs Iron
Company. William Gwinn Mather became president of
the combined corporation, a position which he held for
the next 42 years. Slight, keen-eyed, intense, positive and
assured in manner and courteous in bearing, he learned
his trade thoroughly and grew up with it from its crude
scoop-up-and-ship days to its immensely involved scientific and technical operations of the present day.

Mather took naturally and wholeheartedly to the ore
business and apparently never hesitated or considered an
alternative career. He loved the great North Country. The
first and roughest period was over by the time he began
his work. Marquette was firmly established as an important port, and had already become somewhat famous as a
watering place and summer resort attracting "health seekers, pleasure seekers, artists and tourists." It was not a
romantic writer of folders for a tourist agency, but the

Commissioner of Mineral Statistics for the State of Michigan in his annual statistical report for the year 1877-1878 who said of Marquette, "The excellent hotels afford ample accommodation for travelers and sojourners. The cool salubrious air brings health and vigor to the enervated frame. The speckled denizens of the mountain brooks tempt to piscatorial wanderings and gratify the epicurean appetite; while everywhere abound unbroken forest, the rugged hills, the rocky gorges, the impenetrable glens, the picturesque lakes and beautiful waterfalls, to delight the artist and, in the fullest measure, afford to the lover of nature, in her wildest aspects, the enjoyment which he seeks."

The commissioner, Mr. Charles E. Wright, also pointed out that this city on the curving sweep of shore line at the base of low wooded mountains, "abounds in evidences of prosperity, intelligence and cultivated taste. Its large and elegant high school building constructed of the handsome brownstone from the quarries in the city, roofed with the dark blue slate from Huron bay; its fine church edifices, hotels, business blocks and private dwellings, some of them also of brownstone with slated roofs; its clean, well-paved and shaded streets; the pure water drawn from the cool depths of Lake Superior; the streets and dwellings lighted with gas; the ample facilities for transportation and communication, afforded by railway, lines of steamboats, vessels and telegraph, place it among the most favored cities of a state everywhere noted as abounding in charming villages and thriving cities."

Back on the range Ishpeming had outgrown its neigh-bor Negaunee to become the largest town on the Upper Peninsula. It was the business center for some of the largest and most important mines. It had a fine new school building, roofed with Huron Bay slate, large blocks of stores, foundries and machine shops. It boasted the best hotel in the region (as it still does) and the most attractive dwellings in the mining district. Railroad tracks extended from the main lines to all the mines. And on farther west the village of Michigamme, strung along the shores of its beautiful lake, though completely burned down by a forest fire sweeping out of the woods in 1872, had been rebuilt and now had a population of 1,300. L'Anse had just become a shipping port for ore from the Michigamme mines and had been connected with a rail-road running across the iron range from Marquette.

Both Ishpeming and Negaunee, after two decades of growth, had taken on the appearance of permanent towns. They were still on the frontier, however, and there would be a full lifetime of opportunity for their growth, im-provement and refinement to challenge Mather's passion for order and neatness and pride in happy and more gracious surroundings. He would also be working in a larger and more competitive setting as the dimensions of the industry grew and spread onto the other ore ranges around Lake Superior. In rapid succession during the years when Mather was getting his training and taking on his responsibilities, the Menominee and the Gogebic deposits were explored and the first openings made into their ore bodies.

The enormous demands for ore through the 1860's and up to the Panic of 1873 had stimulated production and spurred on the search for more deposits. Thanks to Douglass Houghton's foresight in requiring the surveyors to keep notes of magnetic deflections and record the altitudes, valuable hints were conveyed to the explorers. United States surveyor Harvey Mellen in his report for 1851 recorded that while running the lines in the vicinity of present Iron River and Stambaugh he had come on an "outcrop of iron ore five feet high on the west face of Stambaugh Hill." Prospectors guided by these reports tramped through the woods over the section lines with a dip compass in one hand and a pick in the other eagerly scouting for ore. They examined outcrops, boulders and ledges. In due course they had outlined the rich Menominee Range, which was located from 30 to 50 miles to the south of the Marquette. U.S. 2 runs through it. It began roughly 40 miles west of Escanaba at Loretto and continued northwest through Vulcan, Norway and Quinnesec to Iron Mountain, and then through a thin region to another area of abundance around Iron River and Stambaugh.

More speculators, breathing the potent air of rumor, again rushed in during the 1870's. Many of the prospects proved to be ephemeral, and others failed because of in-

adequate capital, poor management or improper exploration of the quality and the extent of the deposits. But a
few succeeded.

The story of the development of the Menominee
Range follows the outline of that on the Marquette. The
first ore was hauled out by sleigh through the snow-filled
forests. The combined interests of ore and timber (for
this was the center of the lumbering industry of the day)
attracted the railroads; and the railroads, encouraged both
by large land grants and by the rising volume of business
in prospect, pushed through more lines. They brought
one down from Negaunee to Escanaba in 1864, a branch
of the expanding network of the Chicago & Northwestern, and in 1877 tapped the Menominee Range. The big
Vulcan Mine began producing in 1874, the Norway in
1877 and the Iron Mountain district in 1878. Iron River
and Stambaugh began shipments in 1882, following discoveries in 1878 and the extension of the railway westward. Escanaba was the outlet port. Both the railroad
and lake-shipping men, urged of course by the lumber
and ore men, sought a harbor on Lake Michigan to save
the long journey up the Sault and around the Upper
Peninsula. Escanaba on the west shore of Little Bay de
Noc was the ideal location. Docks were built, a big and
costly charcoal blast furnace was erected by the Cascade
Iron Company, and, along with its lumber industry and
its fisheries, Escanaba became a port city of importance
on the Peninsula second only to Marquette.

The same westward drive that had opened up the Marquette and Menominee ranges also led the explorers into the Gogebic Range in the early 1880's. J. L. Norrie found the ore body in the vicinity of Ironwood in 1884. Prospectors moved in with a rush and soon defined the area of soft red hematite ore, averaging 51 per cent iron, centering around Ironwood, Bessemer and Wakefield. Twelve mines were opened during the first three years after the discovery. The first shipments went down over the new branch line of the railroad to Escanaba in 1885. Then the Chicago & Northwestern Railway built a line down from the port town of Ashland, Wisconsin, only about 40 miles away, to tap the new range. For the expense of hauling bulk ore is so great by rail and so cheap by boat that the cargo must be got to a shiploading dock by the shortest possible route. Ashland became another great shipping port on Lake Superior for the ore trade of the 1880's.

Meanwhile there were all sorts of difficult and demanding problems to be faced and solved. They taxed the best and most inventive minds in the industry to solve them promptly and boldly, at the same time accepting heavy calculated risks. They were pointed up sharply by the Panic of 1873 that shook the whole nation, and by the failure of Jay Cooke's Northern Pacific venture, which brought paralysis and gloom to the ore region. The panic followed one of the most feverish booms in the history of the country. For ten years the lumberjacks and millmen had been working to capacity to get out timber for the insatiable market. Schooners, propellers, steamships, barges—almost anything that would float and carry freight—spread every sail and plied all steam back and forth across the lakes, dumping one cargo and taking on another in the shortest possible time. New furnaces were built at inflated prices and fired to capacity. The mines were worked to the limit, and night and day the ore slid out of the docks through the pockets into waiting holds. People besieged the United States Land Office with applications for maps and information about ore and timber-lands, and for "entries." Then the crash came. Nobody down below wanted iron and the furnaces closed. The fires in new and expensive blast furnaces in the Peninsula went out and the mines were crippled. Many of the new mines, marginal in the sense of meager capital, poor management or low-quality ore, had to suspend altogether. Traffic on the lakes dwindled to a mere trickle and many of the lines had to tie up their boats.

For the mines in stronger position this stringent period turned out to be an incentive to more careful and systematic procedures, and the introduction of scientific processes to take the place of the haphazard methods of the early period of prosperity. It put a premium on skill and knowledge, and cleared away some of the encumbrances of boom speculation. In some cases mines had been opened into ore bodies without any previous determination of their extent or value. One might take such a gamble in an open pit, but not in a shaft where heavy expenditures had to be made before there could be any yield. Skilled analysts and engineers were now required

FOREST CONSERVATION WITH SELECTIVE CUTTING

COAL DOCK AT DULUTH. THE LARGEST PLANT AND OF ITS KIND

to test the product and guide the operations. Common labor with strong back and arms could do the work in the open pits, but intelligent and experienced miners were needed underground. New methods of exploratory drilling and expensive machinery had to be devised to guide the operations and determine where the heavy capital outlay was warranted. The day of the amateur was over, in fact, and the period of the expert and thoroughly qualified operators had begun.

Fortunately for the ore business, costs fell off with the depression to offset the shrinking price of the product. Wages were lower, transportation rates were cut, and by exercising rigid economies the stronger and well-established companies survived the ordeal and emerged from it with new vigor. America was getting accustomed to the boom-and-bust cycle. Panics were troublesome and annoying, and individually disastrous, but they halted only temporarily the onward and upward sweep of the nation. And as the country entered on the 1880's, the shipments of ore, which had dropped to 891,257 tons in 1875, again soared past the million mark to reach two and a half million in 1885 and an additional 1,000,000 tons the following year. This output was attended by prodigious changes and advances in the methods of mining ore. The Mathers and the Cleveland company were among the leaders in transition.

The mines, as we have noted, began to go underground in the 1870's. Explorations had failed to reveal any further large surface deposits. There was a considerable quantity of lean ore near the surface, but no practical technique had been invented to utilize it. An experiment was tried at the Jackson Mine in 1880. The company erected a concentration plant on Partridge Creek opposite the mine to crush the rock and separate the hematite from the jasper. But the jaws of the crusher quickly wore out, and the device for separating the iron oxide from the silica was ineffective. The experiment failed; it would have to wait on a whole aggregation of scientific advances in chemistry, metallurgy and mechanics before it could be put to economic use.

Better results attended the deepening of the pits and the sinking of the shafts. The Jackson Mine had gone on down its inclined floor under its increasing overburden pursuing the rich ore. Long side drifts or tunnels had been driven into the sides from the main pathways deep in the pit. High narrow walls of shining jasper towered above the open passages, and the whole structure trembled and shook when the blasts went off in the workings. The miners wore candles, made in the factory at Negaunee, in their caps to give them light. The Cleveland company had pushed still farther underground in its mines in the late 1870's. One of its larger pits, beginning as a surface outcrop, dipped off to the southwest at a 25-degree angle, and therefore got deeper and deeper as the ore was removed. It was 150 feet wide and 300 feet long. At that point it went under the massive quartzite roof into a workings that, in 1878, reached 400 feet west and 250 feet north and south. The ore vein itself varied from

10 to 40 feet in thickness and averaged nearly 70 per cent metallic iron and only 1.62 per cent silica. The miners left huge pillars of this ore in place to keep the heavy roof from falling in. The ore was hoisted up inclines with machinery built at the Iron Bay Foundry in Marquette.

The Michigan commissioner, after visiting all the mines of the Peninsula, had special words of commendation for the Cleveland workings. "The fine condition of the mine, and the few accidents that have occurred, as well as the completeness of the mine appointments, and the perfect system in all the details of the management, coupled with the good will of the employes towards the employers, reflect much credit upon the agent and the superintendent of the mine. . . . Iron mining, as simple as it may appear to some, is not a business suited to novices." The commissioner also jotted down the significant note that at the Cleveland mine "for the past season (1877-78) they have been using, quite extensively, the diamond drill in boring holes down at different points, to determine the position of the ore stratum. Some of the results have been very interesting. . . ."

Other big mines, like the Champion and the Republic, had gone still farther underground in shafts following the incline of the footwall. From these skipways the miners drove the openings, "drifts," back into the ore bodies at different levels. By 1877 the Champion had taken on the appearance of a full-scale underground mine. On the fourth level of this workings they had entered a formation over 100 feet thick. We could not do better than call on an eyewitness account of the scene as it appeared at that time to Commissioner Wright.

Standing on the edge of a stope and facing west, we look downward and see here and there in the apparent far distance, the moving to and fro of the small lamps of the busy miners, whose forms are only dimly outlined by the feeble rays, making them appear more like evil spirits; an impression which is enhanced by the clanging of the drills and hammers, the heavy reports of the blasts, the rumbling of the skips moving up and down the shafts, and all these sounds echoed and re-echoed from invisible walls, pillars and roof, create in the mind an impression akin to awe and fear. It must be a strange feeling to one not accustomed to mines to creep around in such gloomy places, realizing that if their light should become extinguished by a sudden draught of air or from some unlucky drop of water, they dare not move a single step, since a false one might send them headlong upon the jagged blocks of ore below. With this great width of vein it requires the very best judgment and skill to win the maximum amount of ore and still leave the roofs and sides perfectly secure. . . . Center pillars have been left, which are connected by strong arches sprung to buttresses left on the sides opposite these pillars, and the pillars themselves are also connected by arches.

The same kind of operation was going on at the Republic Mine. This company under the direction of David Morgan, its president, had gone a step farther and installed compressed-air engines and hoisting drums. The compressors were located nearly a mile away at the falls in the Michigamme River, where two turbines placed under a 16-foot head of water developed 700 horsepower. The air was then conducted to the mine through a 15-inch wrought-iron pipe to run the engines and drilling machines and improve the ventilation. The installation cost nearly $100,000, but it furnished cheap power. It represented the brief but efficient transition from the old hand operations to modern electric power in the mines. And all these developments and improvements bore out the prediction of the reports made in 1873 that, though underground mining could not then be undertaken at a profit, methods and machinery could be devised to make it pay.

11

OPERATION UNDERGROUND

The introduction of underground mining brought far-reaching consequences. They all went hand in hand, each dependent on the others. In the earlier period a group of men could get together a few thousand dollars, hire some laborers and begin to quarry ore from the wall of the outcrop. But shaft mining was no game for small operators. Millions of dollars in capital had to be found to set up the machinery and equipment. The industry moved toward consolidation with a few companies commanding large resources replacing a multitude of small firms. And only by the most carefully considered efficiencies could these offset the increased capital investments by lower mining costs. Again the pace and the competition increased.

Still more accurate knowledge of the nature and the extent of the ore deposits was essential. The first maps, surprisingly good under the circumstances, were made by following the outcroppings and charting the pits. A few years of experience, however, had shown how impossible it was to predict the underground contortions of the enfolding rock. The diamond drill was a godsend. It was first used on the range by the Cleveland company in 1877 in the attempt to forecast a three to five-year layout for a mining plan. The drill cut out a neat core which could be lifted up intact and laid on the ground. This precise sample of various strata under the surface revealed accurately the location and depth of the ore body, and the nature and quality of the overburden through which the shaft would have to be sunk to reach it. By sinking these holes at strategic spots on the supposed location, the geologists could forecast the potential tonnage in a given area.

The great Cliffs Shaft Mine, which has no outcrop, was discovered by this method of diamond drilling. The first shaft was put down in 1880 and the second in 1884. It dropped through 60 feet of quicksand and reached the deposit of hard specular hematite at about 400 feet. It has been the largest producer of this type of ore in the country, sending up over 15 million tons in its nearly 70 years of exploitation. Since 1898 its shafts have hoisted ore every year, setting a record for continuous production. The shafts are a fifth of a mile deep and the workings on nearly a score of levels have driven an intricate system of tunnels and stopes through a block of ground more than 10,000 feet long east and west, half a mile wide north and south and 700 feet thick.

The distinguished geologist Charles R. Van Hise, after studying the intricate formations of the range, proposed the theory that the iron ore had been formed by the leaching action of ground water. As it flowed along through the structural rock troughs it produced the local concentration of iron oxide. Following up this theory, and guided by the data provided by the diamond drills, he produced a masterly paper on "The Marquette Iron-Bearing District of Michigan," and a detailed map. This, along with many other individual company explorations, served as an invaluable but never infallible guide to the operations.

Assured by this scientific knowledge of what lay underground, the companies could now afford to take the next step in investment: They erected permanent buildings to house the long-term operations. A few tentative beginnings had been made rather early. When the Cleveland company had sunk its first small shaft 75 feet deep in 1866, there was a shaft house above it, built like a pyramid, 40 feet high, operating two skips of three ton capacity; as one came up, the other went down. These were small and experimental. Bigger things were required. The Michigamme Company built a solid stone engine and shaft house on the footwall side of its ore vein and got its machinery operating in 1878. And from that time on shaft houses sprang up all along the range to become the most characteristic feature of the landscape. The Cleveland company built a brownstone engine house and shops at its mine in 1882.

The engine house contained hoisting machinery for the various mines. The shafts for reaching the ore and for hauling it to the surface were still driven down the incline of the footwall. But the disclosure of ore bodies buried under the earth with no outcroppings led immediately to the vertical shafts. The first shafts were sunk directly down into the ore deposit. This turned out to be hazardous and costly because the overlying rocks would sink down or cave in under the immense overhead pressure when the ore was removed, and damage the shafts. The solution of this was to drive the shafts down through the rock at the edge of the ore body on the footwall side and dig tunnels off horizontally into the ore.

This operation required more machinery: power drills, hoisting and conveying apparatus, pumps and ventilation systems and better lighting. Wood & Wearing steam drills were introduced in 1876. The Rand power drill came into general use a few years later. The first electric lights were installed in 1880. The Cleveland company built an electric-lighting plant, equipped with a Brush (of Cleveland) electric-light machine of 18 lamps. It was a great advance in safety and convenience and in aiding the sorting of the ore for shipping and stock-piling. The Cornish pumps, once so arresting to the eye in the iron country, were in almost universal use to keep the mines free from water. They generally stood 50 or more feet high, and by using one low-pressure and one high-pressure cylinder they could pump 3,000 or more gallons of water per minute. The old Chapin Mine Cornish pump has been left standing as a tourist attraction at Iron Mountain on the Menominee Range.

Rock drills and dynamite were required in the hard-ore mines. The heavy blasting made the earth tremble four times a day. In a letter to Mr. Mather, in 1870, the agent wrote concerning one of the men, "Mr. Mills has constantly objected to the building of a house for himself and says now he doesn't care for it. I am confident, however, that he would feel more secure in the safety of his family if they lived more remote from the mines, as they are now obliged for safety to go down cellar every time we blast, which is four times a day."

The method of mining was still relatively simple. The men drilled a tunnel from the shaft into the ore body and mined out big rooms in the ore, leaving enough pillars to hold up the roof. This was known as the "open-stope" method. It wasted much of the ore. Where the roof was weak, and in the soft ore mines, timbers were set up to retain the openings and to prevent the accidental fall of ore. This method became known as the "square-set" system. As soon as a room about seven feet square had been mined, heavy timber legs were set up in the four corners. These were capped and sided with boards to prevent the fall of broken material. From this first set the mining proceeded upward another seven feet or so, another set of timber legs was placed on top of the first, and so on to the limit of the vein, with a lining of timber replacing the deposit of ore.

The "caving system" was evolved from experimental beginnings at the Cleveland Hematite Mine to the south of Teal Lake in 1881. In that year the Cleveland Iron Mining Company bought this property, which had been worked as an open-pit mine to a depth of 120 feet. The company sank two shafts down through rock to the ore body. The deposit was blocked out into a series of horizontal layers. After taking out the top sublevel, the miners blasted out the timbers and allowed the roof and overburden to cave in under its own weight. Then they moved down to the next lower sublevel and repeated the process. The tramway was kept on the next lower level and the ore, as it was mined, was sent down through a special chute into the cars. The method proved so successful that it was widely studied, and, with improvements that grew out of experience, it became, and still is, a common practice. The cars in the mines were at first loaded and pushed by hand. The first electric haulage was introduced in 1892 at the Cleveland Lake Mine.

The shift from handwork to machinery posed seriously the problem of power. It took rising quantities of horsepower to lift and lower the skips into and out of the shafts with thousands of tons of waste dirt, rock and sand as well as the usable ore; to pump out water and pump in air; move the cars in the tunnels and drifts; and convey the men up and down at the end of the shifts. We have noted how the Republic Mine installed compressed air by using water at a falls a mile away. This was a partial answer to the problem, but only transitional. For the era of electricity was coming in rapidly.

Young William G. Mather was keenly interested in electric-power development from the very beginning. The whole region abounds in waterfalls. The streams plunge down over the escarpments and through gorges dropping

800 feet on their short journeys from the range hills to Lake Superior. At several points along the Carp and the Dead rivers, at the foot of Deer Lake and Silver Lake which feed into them, on the Au Train River and at Michigamme there were ideal sites for dams, storage basins and generating plants. Mather had been over the ground himself. He had also sent out his own agent to explore it. A letter to him from F. P. Mills, dated September 28, 1887, reports that "the Dead River where we crossed is 35 feet wide and 2 feet deep and flows 65 feet per minute on top of water in middle of stream. This would give us with a 90-ft. fall about 400 Horse Power. . . . Have written for abstracts and will let you know who owns the land. We have had no rain and the river is very low."

It took some time for the plan to mature. The first electric power was generated by steam from plants using coal shipped in at considerable expense from the mines down below. Mather did not lose sight of his long-range objective, however. We have an interesting record of the care and vigor with which he pursued it. He and his friend William Gerhauser of Detroit went abroad together in the summer of 1901. Gerhauser had pioneered in the mining of iron ore and the manufacture of charcoal pig iron, beginning in the 1870's. Their primary interest was to talk with the ironmakers and ore producers of England and Sweden and see their plants and operations. They did not get much from their English colleagues. A typical entry in their rather full journal of the trip reads,

"Mr. Blackwell, who received us rather coldly, gave us very little information regarding their business, the irons they were using, or anything else. . . . Manufacturers are secretive, and not disposed to make changes, being satisfied with their products, and the material entering into its composition."

The story was different in Sweden. At the big mine at Grängesberg, Mather was much impressed by the use of electric power in all the operations of mining, hoisting, conveying, crushing, pumping and separating. The power was all developed by waterfall at three stations and was transmitted from ten to 15 miles to a central transformer station and there distributed as required. The power was costing them only $20 per horsepower per annum. A pumping station 443 feet underground was working satisfactorily under electric power. Skips, each hoisting five tons, were driven by electric motors. A separating system, far in advance of anything in use in America, recovering 600 tons of good ore each day, was electrically operated. Equally impressive to Mather and his friend was the Dannemora Mine, the oldest iron-ore mine in the world, with authentic records of operation going back a thousand years. The open pit was then 1,000 feet long, 50 to 200 feet wide and 500 feet deep. There were also three shafts reaching down 900 feet and a Cornish pump to keep the water out. Everything was powered by hydroelectric generators at the waterfalls.

It is clear that this visit of inspection made a deep imprint on Mather's thinking. He began to lay plans for

harnessing the water on the range and making it produce
the power required for the mines and the growing towns.
Steam turbines were installed at Negaunee in 1909 and
transmission lines on steel towers were stretched to the
mines. The steam installation was to be used as a reserve
in case of drought or low-water periods at the dams. In
the meantime, Mather had selected a spot on the Au
Train River, about 15 miles from Munising, as the site
for the first water-power development. It was built in
1910, and produced 1,200 horsepower. It was followed
the next year by a plant on the Carp River, about a mile
from Marquette. With a head of 600 feet, it could produce 7,400 horsepower. The huge five-foot iron pipes
which carry the water from the dam down the hill to this
Carp plant were made in Germany and shipped all the
way out to Marquette. The seams were hammer-and-
anvil-welded with flawless workmanship, and are still
strong and tight after 40 years of service. A third unit
was constructed on Dead River, four miles north of
Negaunee, in 1916. These modern power plants were
the beginning of the network for the Upper Peninsula,
and they brought into the service of the mines abundance
of electricity to keep the ever-growing operations supplied
with power.

Electricity also transformed the working conditions
underground and eventually made the tunnels and drifts
a little less unpleasant than the subway tubes of a modern
city. We have already observed with Commissioner
Charles E. Wright the eerie scene in one of the early

mining rooms where the flickering candles of the miners'
caps threw pale spots of light into the dark cavern. Water
oozed from the side walls of these early mines and
drained down along the edges of the drift or tunnel, making a muddy floor at the sides of the tramways. Miles of
ladders, reddened with water and mud from climbing
boots, led from one level to another. The men changed
into their leather boots and mining clothes at home and
returned there grimed with red dust to wash away the
stains of the day's work. The candles in their caps gave
way to brighter carbide lights, and these in turn to brilliant lamps powered by storage batteries like flashlights.
Mather built special dry houses with showers and running
water for the men to change in so that they might go
home looking clean and comfortable. And the chain of
electric lights strung through all the connecting tunnels
of the mines removed from the underground workings
any appearance of "evil spirits" flitting about in a gloomy
Vulcan's cave.

Many of the miners preferred the uniform and cool
temperature underground to the varied discomforts on
the surface and developed a brotherhood and *esprit de
corps* all their own. They were also bound together by a
pride in craftsmanship. A square-set stope at the head
wall of a drift was no place for the inexperienced. This
was technical work for the expert "underground men."
French Canadians got claustrophobia down there and
flatly refused to work below surface. Skilled Cornishmen
felt at home in the workings and were well content to

take over the job. They came over from the worn-out mines of their native lands, or up from older American mining settlements. They brought with them their own vocabulary of mining terms, many of which they fixed into the speech of the iron range and are unavoidably used in this book. They contributed their word *tail* or *tailings* for the waste products, *horse* for the columns of rock in the ore veins, *jig* for the vibrating machine that separates the crushed ore, *skip* for the bucket or elevator which is lowered into the shaft to bring up the ore and *sump* for the basin where the water is collected in the mine.

The Cornishmen were among the greatest of the mining captains, those immensely able underground technicians who were always observing and studying the progress of the workings, and seemed, almost by intuition, to follow the crazy convolutions of the rock formations. It was a matter of high personal ambition with them to get out at least expense the maximum amount of clean ore, to avoid digging through waste rock and to guard the safety of the miners. Experienced geologists learned to listen carefully to the words of these experienced captains on the nature and position of the ore deposits. The captains were held in great respect by the men who might stop work when they came into the drifts just to show their independence, but would touch their caps and address them as Captain when they met them on the surface. They contributed their bits to the improvement of mining methods. Captain Collick was noted for his in-

WOOD-BURNING LOCOMOTIVE DAYS, JACKSON MINE

STEAM AND DIESEL MOTIVE POWER

Photograph by Henry Mayer

vention of the Cleveland-Cliffs Sheet-Iron Sconce (another Cornish usage for candlestick), a device for shielding the candle flame on the miner's cap. Several of the Cornishmen became famous, even legendary, on the range for their physical strength, their ability to wrestle, handle a drill or load more ore than the next man.

Captain or miner, they all seemed to be akin and were called by everyone "Cousin Jack." The term became generic and was lower-cased to plain cousin jack. They went willingly down into the mines carrying their day's ration of candles and their lunch of pasty—that remarkable piece of piecrust wrapped round a full diet of meat and vegetables and baked in the oven. At noon they placed their pasty on a shovel and warmed it over the candle flames, and then washed it down with a tin cup full of tea. Warm human tales of the Cornishmen are still told on the iron range to keep the memory of these hardy and colorful men alive. They worked the mines in those early years and brought them to a high state of production. Many of them moved on in the 1890's and their places were taken by another group of skilled miners from Finland, Sweden and Norway.

The underground mines devoured quantities of timber and gave employment to lumberjacks and carpenters. This demand came, of course, while the furnaces were still consuming acres of forests to make charcoal iron, while millions of feet were being shipped out for building purposes and the chemical plants were learning the uses of wood products. A new strain was placed on the forest reserves. Some of the mines had to use .72 cubic feet of timber for each ton of ore taken out, others as much as .92 cubic feet. Logs three or four feet in diameter were set up at regular short intervals along the tunnels and in the rooms, and very heavy, thick boards were laid on them to retain the roof and walls. They had to be strong enough to hold the weight and yet resilient and yielding enough to give gradually under the enormous pressure of the slow-moving overburden which cannot be restrained. The permanent passageways became a solid tunnel of timber along the sides and roof. The square-sets required particularly large and sturdy logs and planks as they reached up, one timber set on another, through the ore to heights of 40 and sometimes close to 100 feet. The log and timber pile outside the shaft looked almost as big as the stock pile of ore, and the quantities going down on the skip seemed as great as the ore loads coming up.

Timber did not last long underground. It had to be pulled out and replaced at intervals. The air was limited and low in oxygen content, there was no light and the moisture content was too little or too great. The pressure on the timber was continuous. Curious foamlike molds appeared on the wood and it rotted away. The companies had to acquire more forest land and bring in more timber, frequently over long hauls from woods to mines.

All this adjunct work and material added to the cost of mining ore. And it came just at the time when the fabulous deposits suited to the simpler open-pit mining were being discovered and opened to exploitation in the Vermilion and Mesabi ranges lying northwest of Duluth.

12

VERMILION AND MESABI

ALL through the years we have been describing the nation continued to surge on west and northwest. State and federal surveyors moved on ahead to run the section and township lines just as Houghton and Burt had done on the Upper Peninsula. Right behind them, or even along with them, went the timber cruisers to locate the heavy stands of pine timber for the waiting sawmills of the country. And also following them along were the geologists looking for more mineral deposits. They got up into northwest Wisconsin in the 1850's and on into Minnesota west and northeast of the lake head in the 1860's.

The port and outfitting station was at the mouth of the St. Louis River where the city of Duluth was founded. The old Fond du Lac trading post of Astor's day was on up the river a short distance at the head of navigation. The year after the Sault Canal was opened there were a half-dozen families living there. Oneota, the settlement of the Merritt family who played such a dramatic role in opening up the Mesabi Range, had about 20 inhabitants

145

and a few workshops, a store and a sawmill. Minnesota Point was the site of a trading post set up in 1852 by George Stuntz, another of the great names in the Minnesota iron rush of later years. Duluth was formed by the union of little settlements like these in 1857. From then on to the Panic of 1873 Duluth was a scene of rather feverish activity which centered not on iron ore but around railroads, timber and wheat. Handsome new steamers brought excursions and regular passenger runs up through the Sault to Duluth, so magnificently set on its shelf above the lake with the timbered slopes and sheer rock cliffs rising sharply behind it. Jay Cooke undertook the building of the Lake Superior and Mississippi River Railroad from Duluth to the south. Alexander McDougall sailed the *Meteor* to Duluth in 1868 and 1869 and the *Japan* in 1871 and following years. He brought up Jay Cooke's engineering party that had charge of the Duluth end of the railroad. He sailed up with rails and carried back wheat. The first docks were for this kind of cargo. The ships at that time carried a stern yawl boat to locate the channel at Minnesota Point, and they lightered passengers and freight in from anchorage, landing them on the gravel beach.

While Duluth was struggling along with these projects and problems, up and down along with the national booms and panics, reports came down from the explorers and geologists back in the hills 75 miles to the north. The Vermilion Indian trail ran up the escarpment, across the rough terrain, through the forests and muskeg to Vermilion Lake up near the Canadian border. Richard and his brother Henry Eames, reconnaissance surveyors, were exploring the geology along the trail. In the vicinity of the lake they found a bed of exceedingly hard iron ore exposed to a width of from 50 to 60 feet. They found also some specimens of pyrites, sulphur and iron, "fool's gold," which they mistook for the genuine precious metal. No one paid much attention to the ore outcrop, but hundreds of men swarmed into Duluth, outfitted themselves for prospecting and joined in an exciting gold rush across the Indian trail. They soon returned disillusioned.

George Stuntz suspected the truth, but he, too, went up to see the minerals. He was a man of unusual ability and experience, who had surveyed township lines in Wisconsin for the Government, and had then moved on to Duluth to run section lines in Minnesota. He had studied archaeology as an amateur, and he knew a good deal about rock formations and minerals. He was tough, wiry and completely at home in the woods. He tramped up the trail, looked at the "gold" and pronounced it iron. Then he explored the region, examined the thick outcropping and was immediately convinced that here was another of the rich deposits of iron ore which were being uncovered around Lake Superior's ancient rock rim.

The whole episode reminds us of Everett's journey up the Carp River to Teal Lake to find Marji-Gesick's iron mountain. Stuntz brought back samples. He got his Duluth friend George Stone interested in the prospect.

They showed the specimens to Eastern men: to Surveyor General George B. Sargeant, who had been in charge of the Wisconsin surveys and with whom Stuntz had worked; and to Charlemagne Tower, a millionaire entrepreneur of Pottsville, Pennsylvania. Tower was willing to invest if further scientific inspection recommended it, for the ore was good. State Geologist Newton H. Winchell went over the area in 1878 and made a glowing report. Tower sent his own geologist, Professor Albert H. Chester of Hamilton College, to the location, and after his second exploration he advised the operation. Tower then formed in 1882 the Minnesota Iron Company, including in it his son Charlemagne, Jr., Stone and Stuntz. They got a charter for a railway to reach back from Lake Superior to the proposed location. Surveyor Stuntz himself located the route. It came down from the ore deposits through extremely rough country, over hills, through rocks and forest, to meet the lake 27 miles east of Duluth at Two Harbors, named for Agate and Burlington bays which form a single protected harbor. It cost around $2,000,000 to clear and grade the 70-mile route and lay the rails, and for a time it almost threw Tower into bankruptcy.

The company built a huge ore dock, the largest yet constructed, seven feet higher than the one at Marquette, at a cost of $200,000. They brought in over $300,000 worth of machinery and plant for the mines. They sailed in by scow a locomotive named the *Three Spot*, which is still on display at Two Harbors as a museum piece. Everything was ready for traffic in 1884.

In the meantime Stuntz had led a crew of men back to the location with drills, picks, shovels, black powder and other equipment to make some test openings for the mine. He opened up the Soudan Mine above Stuntz Bay on Lake Vermilion on the western end of the range. And on June 30, 1884, with ten cars and a coach for the official party placed on the siding, and with the *Three Spot* steamed up ready to haul them down the new railroad, the Cornish mine boss wheeled on the first load of ore while the distinguished visitors and a band of Chippewa Indians looked on. The railroad was named the Duluth & Iron Range, and some years later it did actually enter Duluth.

Charlemagne Tower, Jr., moved out to Minnesota to give active direction to the company's business. Recognizing Stuntz's genius as a surveyor and cruiser and mineralogist, Tower employed him as agent to buy up land on the Vermilion Range. Stuntz did his work well. He was able to locate and buy for the company 17,000 acres of the richest deposits for $40,000 in and around the Soudan Mine. The range turned out to be only about 15 miles long, but it contained a heavy concentration of ore that reached far down into the earth to depths of 1,500 to 2,000 feet. Over 30,000,000 tons of high-quality ore were taken out during the next 25 years. This first mine produced as follows:

Year	Tons
1884	62,124
1885	225,484
1886	307,948
1887	394,910

Then the Chandler and the Pioneer mines at Ely, on the eastern end of the range, were opened up and the shipments rose:

1888	511,953
1889	844,638

The range happened to be the oldest one geologically in the Lake Superior region. The ore was so granite-hard at the west end that the miners had trouble getting holes drilled into it for blasting. It was much softer on the east. Settlements grew up around the locations, and within a few years the Vermilion Range was the scene of lively activities with the population centering at Soudan, Tower and Ely.

By jumping all the way from Duluth to Vermilion Lake, the prospectors had passed by the most fabulous of all the ore deposits, and one of the greatest concentrations so far discovered in the world, the Mesabi Iron Range. In fact the Minnesota Iron Company had unsuspectingly built the Duluth & Iron Range Railroad straight across the east end of the Mesabi. The existence of the range was fairly well known, however, despite its extreme isolation 75 to 100 miles back of Duluth in the toughest kind of terrain. Timber cruisers had picked up fragments of iron as they scouted through the forests estimating the potential yield of lumber. Both the Minnesota and the U. S. geologists had gained a fair preliminary concept of the rock formations during their first surveys of the area. Their annual reports show clearly that they suspected there were ore deposits on this range. But they were not hunting locations for the mining companies. One of them wrote into his report, "It is not the business of the state geological survey to find iron mines; that is the business of the explorer. A geologist's duty is by study and observation to indicate the proper conditions for ore deposits and the geographic limits of the formations in which those conditions exist. The intelligent and unbigoted explorer will assimilate these ideas and apply them in discovering the stores of hidden wealth. The work of sinking test-pits is work of exploration, not geological work. . . . We confess that we take considerable pride in the fact that our predictions in regard to the Mesabi are now in such rapid process of fulfillment."

Outcrops at various spots along the range had been known at least since 1875. Many iron experts had actually made the arduous journey back over the hills to examine them. Charlemagne Tower's geologist, Professor Chester, had visited this range in that year 1875. Another great expert, Captain A. P. Wood, had gone up to the very spot where the first big discovery was later made.

They, like many others, reported that the ore was not worth bothering about. They unanimously discouraged investments and operations in this region. The trouble, of course, was that they knew too little about the geological structure of this iron deposit. It is overlaid with glacial drift from a few inches to 100 feet in depth. The outcrop rocks were very low in iron content—too "thin" to be of value. But farther down, hidden from superficial inspection, lay thick layers of paint rock, red ore, yellow ocher, hard blue ore, soft blue ore, brown ore and mixtures of brown and yellow ocher or soft blue, in an indescribable fairyland of color and an ironman's dream of the inconceivable.

It fell to the lot of the famous Merritt boys from the Oneota settlement at Duluth to discover this treasure chest. They were not deterred by some 15 years of adverse opinions by better geologists and miners than they. The Merritts were a remarkable family, deserving of the fine book which Paul De Kruif wrote about them under the title *Seven Iron Men*. The father, Lewis Merritt, was a surveyor and expert timber cruiser who had for years roamed the northern woods, estimating the stands of hard pine for the lumbermen. He had gone up to Vermilion during the gold-rush days and had brought back to Oneota a few samples of ore. He never followed up, except to instruct his sons in the art of prospecting and cruising, and to express his belief in the future of Minnesota as a timber and mineral-producing land.

Five of his seven sons followed in his footsteps—Lewis,

Alfred, Napoleon, Leonidas and Cassius. They lived in
the era of speculative fever that kept Duluth and vicinity
in a state of excitement during the late 1870's and
through the 1880's, and they watched the rapid developments at Vermilion. Ore trains rumbled down every day
to the new docks at Two Harbors, where they dumped
their wealth into waiting freighters. It seemed not impossible to the Merritts that the range of high broken
land to the south, which the Indians called Mesabi, might
also bear ore. They went into the region with new interest, entering it from the northeast.

Starting from Tower on March 17, 1889, with a crew
of six men bearing their own equipment, they went by
way of Pike River and Rice Lake, and hacked their way
into Township 59 North, Range 18 West, Section 34.
They dug test pits there, but found nothing. They were
actually right on the edge of the great deposit, but just
a little too far north. They moved south into the next
tier of sections and tried again. They uncovered heavy
reddish stuff, sandy in appearance and in feel to the
hands. It had the color and weight of iron ore, but it
was so loose that it could be separated with a pick and
scooped up with a shovel. They were disappointed that
it was not hard and sure in quality. Another crew, digging farther east, brought up some of the same formation
at what is now the Biwabik Mine.

Tests soon showed, however, that this curiously formed
material ran up to 60 per cent and more iron ore.
The Merritts engaged a skilled mining captain to direct

further operations. On November 16, 1890, he opened
a test pit right in the heart of the range. He found not
far below the surface soil and gravel a rich body of soft
hematite ore, with every indication that there was plenty
more of it lying below the overburden in all directions.
With singular lack of inventiveness, but with great respect for tradition, the Merritts promptly christened the
place Mountain Iron. They had cut into the range about
30 miles west of its eastern edge, just beyond the great
letter-Z fold in the rock structure at the Virginia Horn.

They followed up on the information repeatedly given
by the state geologists in their conversations and in their
formal reports, which showed the order of stratification
of the rocks in the district, and that the formation, although flat, did contain good ore. They sank more test
pits. With pick and shovel they dug down through the
glacial till as though they were sinking a well. They
timbered the hole down as far as the top of the ore deposit. Then, still with pick and shovel, and generally
without blasting, they drove on through the layers of ore
from 70 to 130 feet, where they were stopped by water.
The material was hoisted out in buckets by a windlass
and dumped round the pit in a circular stock pile. Finally
one man would climb into the bucket with a pick in his
hand, and, as he was slowly lowered into the pit, he would
chip out a groove in the wall to give an accurate "core"
and make measurements. Wherever they explored around
Mountain Iron they found rich ore testing 65 per cent.

The news spread like a Minnesota forest fire through Duluth and across the country.

Mining companies were organized right and left during the next two years, and there was a mad scramble for position and control. From December 1, 1890, to September 1, 1892, 127 companies were incorporated in Minnesota to exploit the iron ore. Most of them floated vast quantities of capital stock, $3,000,000 being the standard for a company. The Merritt boys were among the incorporators in 20 of them. The leases were bought like hot cakes. The Merritts acquired 141 of them during the year 1890. At the same time, they were taking the lead in the hard labors necessary to put the mines into production and to provide transportation facilities to move the ore out of the isolated wilderness and into the holds of the lake freighters at Duluth. This was also a formidable undertaking. It required immense sums of money which the Merritts did not have and did not know where to find. They had more than used up their own stake of $20,000 in the expensive business of exploration, and they had already borrowed heavily for their leases. Nonetheless they sent their crews on to sink more pits west of Mountain Iron, and east in the vicinity of Biwabik while they besieged the banks and searched for capital. Their holdings were without value until a railroad could tap them, and they were determined to go into the big business for themselves.

The railroads nearest to the mine locations were the

Duluth & Iron Range, the Minnesota Iron Company's line which crossed the Mesabi a dozen miles to the east; and the Duluth & Winnipeg, which ran through Grand Rapids, Minnesota, thus making an acute angle with the iron range. The Merritts blazed out a location for a road of their own, one with a downhill haul over easy curves and gradients. Leonidas Merritt went east to try to get backing from Henry C. Frick, of Pittsburgh, who, with Andrew Carnegie, represented one of the most powerful steel interests in America. He failed. He finally raised the money in his home state, Minnesota. With the help of M. B. Harrison, K. D. Chase, Donald Grant and other interested citizens, Leonidas incorporated the Duluth, Missabe & Northern Railroad. With almost superhuman energy they pushed this line through muskeg and forest across the range from Mountain Iron 42 miles to Stony Brook. There it connected, by agreement, with the Duluth & Winnipeg. It was put into operation during the first week of October, 1892, and, amid the usual celebrations, the first trainload of iron ore left the Mesabi for Duluth for vessel shipment to Lake Erie. The D. M. & N. made contracts with the owners and lessees of several of the largest mines in the vicinity. This combination seemed to be a gilt-edged guarantee of future success. They extended the line 18 miles east to serve the Biwabik Mine, and placed heavy orders for locomotives and ore cars.

Riding the dizzy boom of 1892, the Merritts seemed to find nothing too big to undertake. The Minnesota

Iron Company, contrasting their Vermilion holdings of deep-pit, hard-iron ore with these immense Mesabi deposits near the surface which could be scooped up forthwith and shipped, offered the Merritts $8,000,000 for their mine and railroad interests. They refused. And when the Duluth & Winnipeg failed to provide the number of ore cars for which they had contracted, the Merritts, who had already purchased 750 cars of their own, promptly ordered 750 more. They still did not have enough to handle all the ore mined for shipment during the 1893 season. They decided to free themselves from any dependence on the D. & W. road by building their own D. M. & N. line right on down to the harbor. For this part of the huge capital outlay they had promises from Charles W. Wetmore of Wall Street, who was tied in with McDougall's American Steel Barge Company which we have already noted. If the Merritts would ship their ore in this company's barges, Wetmore would get a loan for them.

This deal was arranged in 1892. Contractors were engaged, rails shipped in, the road was laid and thousands of men were at work on Merritt interests. Right in the middle of it all came the sharp and disastrous Panic of 1893, one of the worst in American history. As in 1873, financial houses failed right and left, important firms collapsed, mills and factories closed, thousands of men were thrown out of work, bread lines formed and cash seemed to dry up and disappear. Credit could not be had on any security. The Panic and all its attendant evils hit the iron ranges with rude force. There was no money to pay the men, no income or new loans to keep the companies, just on the verge of great wealth, afloat.

The Panic could not have caught the Merritts at a more critical time. A year earlier their commitments would not have been dangerous; a year later their fundamental and preparatory enterprises might have been completed. In 1893 they were squarely in the middle. Wetmore had to default on his promises. The only person who seemed to have any money for investment was John D. Rockefeller, the financial backer of the American Steel Barge Company. The Merritts got $350,000 from him to carry on. The courts tried later on to find out what happened. The whole transaction was complicated, as we shall see. The Merritts discovered that they did not any longer own the vast interests which the Minnesota Company had wanted to buy a few months earlier for $8,000,000. Alfred brought suit against Rockefeller charging fraud, and won. The case was appealed and the judgment reversed. It was then settled out of court. The sum, said to be a half million dollars, which the Merritts received in the settlement went to their creditors, and they passed out of the drama of Mesabi iron, having contributed to it one of its most exciting and poignant episodes.

America had become accustomed to land booms, gold rushes and mass movements of population. She had seldom seen anything quite like the frenzied descent upon the Mesabi in 1891 and 1892 following the discoveries by the Merritts. Duluth was the port of entry. People poured into it—Eastern millionaires, prospectors and explorers, miners, laborers and lumberjacks. There were only about 3,500 people in Duluth in 1870 when Jay Cooke's Lake Superior & Mississippi Railroad was opened for traffic. Fifteen years later, by the time the Vermilion Range was in operation, the population had soared to about 25,000. In 1890, when Mountain Iron was discovered, it had reached 33,000, and during the next decade it soared to 53,000. Thousands of men were at work building railroads and docks and improving the harbor to receive the lumber, the grain and the iron ore rolling into Duluth and its neighbor Superior for shipment.

In such an atmosphere, with such a mass migration of people, the private misfortune of the Merritt family was a day's wonder quickly absorbed in the grand onward rush of the Mesabi. If one man failed or fell, another was already there on the glacial drift to take his place. A single lease might be a pure speculation, but the ore business as a whole was a guaranteed success. So the process of exploration pushed forward with vigor.

Throughout the winter months of 1891 and 1892 hundreds of men were organized into crews and sent back with sleds loaded with equipment over the snow to the range to sink pits. They climbed on foot up the escarpment and tramped across frozen swamps and through thick forests to locate the range which is 1,500 feet or more above Lake Superior. Men carried supplies on their backs, for they were going into a wilderness from 30 to 100 miles removed from any kind of road. The range itself was not easy to locate. The ore-bearing section averages about half a mile wide. A mantle of glacial drift covered the rocks, and timber and bush obstructed the explorer's view. The ore was not continuous, but deposited in extensive beds. The explorers could be forgiven for sinking a few holes where there was no ore. They cut away the timber, erected scores of log camps and dug hundreds of pits into the ore body during the long sub-zero winters.

They tested the range east and west of Mountain Iron. John McCaskill, one of the best and the luckiest of the explorers, was cruising about over the formation 18 miles farther to the east. Quite by chance he noticed traces of soft ore clinging to the roots of a fallen pine tree. Captain J. A. Nichols, a highly skilled operator, followed up this clue and went there to supervise the testing. He put Captain J. G. Cohoe in charge and sank 15 test pits during the winter 1891-1892. Everywhere they broke into rich 65 per cent ore in the most extensive deposit discovered up to that time. They had found the vast Biwabik deposit. The Biwabik Mountain Iron Company was formed and immediately leased the property. The Biwabik, Cincinnati, Canton, Hale and Kanawa mines were opened into this bed.

In March 1892 this same Captain Cohoe made a test at Missabe Mountain, now the city of Virginia. He struck ore with his first pit only 13 feet under the surface. He quickly spread the tests and revealed another area equal apparently to the Biwabik. Henry W. Oliver, the great plow-and-shovel manufacturer of Pittsburgh, happened to be in Minneapolis attending a Republican convention when he heard the news of this discovery. He went to Duluth to investigate and decided to get into the ore business. In less than four months after the first test pit had been sunk, Oliver had taken a lease of Missabe Mountain on a guaranteed royalty, with a very high royalty rate for those days of 65 cents per ton, based on a minimum of 400,000 tons annually, with a cash advance on royalty of $75,000. This quickly consummated deal brought into the Mesabi one of its most important operators.

Two months after Cohoe's discovery of Missabe, other explorers found new beds in the same township farther west. They were working along the large bend in the green schist ridge which was soon outlined at the Virginia Horn. The test pits showed the deposit to be extensive and rich. A. E. Humphreys & Co. acquired the rights, pursued the exploration and opened the New England, Virginia, Lone Jack, Wyoming and other mines. The mines followed the curving line of the greenstone ridge as it looped sharply back to the northeast and then bent round to assume its former direction toward the southwest. The town of Virginia was started by the Virginia Improvement Company, and it soon became the central town for this whole region.

John M. Longyear got in on the ground floor with

leases in the same region in 1891-1892. He was an explorer of long experience and phenomenal record. He had struck ore on the Marquette Range in the 1870's, he had located it on the Menominee and he had led the profitable search into the Gogebic. He came on to the Mesabi, looked over the tests and took out leases in this same tier of townships. He soon acquired a vast fortune and built for himself a 60-room mansion at Marquette, Michigan. Later on, when the railroad passed too close to his estate, he pulled the mansion down, shipped it to Brookline, Massachusetts, and set it up again to the precise specifications of the original. A productive mine at Hibbing is now named for him—a great honor in the mining country—and the town of Chisholm stretches along the shore of Longyear Lake.

These are samples of the activity going on in this part of the Mesabi while the Merritts were building their railroad, and these were the mines which guaranteed to it all the shipping it could handle. In fact these operators urged the Merritts on to greater speed so that the new ore could get to market. The completion of the road gave further urgency to the search. Explorers followed the loop on down to Eveleth and uncovered more ore in 1893.

Twenty-five miles to the west, above the same rock formation, on the edge of Ranges 20 and 21, was a big roisterous lumber camp. A lumber company had brought in men and a portable sawmill to cut the heavy stand of timber. Shacks had been hastily put up among the stumps and mud to house the lumberjacks. Following his belief that the ore bodies continued in this direction, Frank Hibbing, a young immigrant who had come to the Mountain Iron district from the lumber mills of Wisconsin, made his way down the range to this camp to look for ore. He found some and took out leases. His mining friends around Virginia thought he was crazy when he left those unexploited riches to hack a road through to the new location. They were amazed, in a land where miracles were commonplace, when further tests and later operations revealed his find to be by far the largest single concentration of high-grade ore ever found anywhere. The sorry lumber camp became the town of Hibbing, named for Captain Frank who soon gave it all the improvements of a modern city.

So, bit by bit and bed by bed the great Mesabi Range was defined and opened during the hectic decade of the 1890's. It turned out to be over 100 miles long, extending in a narrow, snakelike strike never more than two miles wide, thinning to nothing in a few places, from Birch Lake on the east through Embarrass, Aurora, Biwabik and Eveleth to Virginia. There it makes its great Z fold and continues west southwest through Mountain Iron, Kinney, Buhl, Chisholm, Hibbing, Keewatin, Nashwauk, Snowball, Calumet, Coleraine, and thins away as it reaches Grand Rapids.

Millions of dollars were poured in from 1892 on. Homes for the miners had to be built at once. These were first built by the companies to be ready to receive the thousands of workers who began to pour in through Duluth and scatter over the range. Many of them came on from the Michigan ranges, attracted by the general excitement and by the opportunities and high wages for skilled miners and bosses in the early competitive days. Before the railroad was opened they had to travel in by sleigh, horseback or on foot, camping on the way. As the demand grew, the labor agents directed immigrant workers to the district. Finns and Scandinavians were soon the dominant groups and became experts in the special techniques of mining developed on the Mesabi.

The thousands of test pits, added to the accumulating body of knowledge gathered by the distinguished group of Minnesota and United States geologists, clarified in detail the peculiar formation of the Mesabi Range. The rocks in which the iron occurs are known as the Huronian series; they were formed in the Pre-Cambrian geologic era and are, therefore, next to the oldest on the earth. They are millions of years old. In the upper portion of the Huronian series is the Biwabik iron formation. The iron-bearing portion of the Biwabik, in general, is in turn composed of four layers. These are called, in order of descent, the Upper Slaty Horizon, Upper Cherty Horizon, Lower Slaty Horizon and Lower Cherty Horizon. Below these come the Pokegama quartzite, then greenstone, slates and granite, and above them Virginia slate, cretaceous conglomerate and shale, and the glacial drift. The ore layers vary in thickness up to 300 feet.

The most generally held theory about them is that they

were laid down in shallow coastal waters through organic agencies. Volcanic action, probably beneath the ocean, precipitated iron carbonate, chert, iron sulphide and other elements. Some of these precipitates hardened, remained unaltered and without much iron content, and are found in superabundance on the range in the form of "taconite." As the land rose in the period of mountain building, these rocks were tilted and folded, inclined and fractured. Erosion began and other portions of the Biwabik iron formation were enriched to high-grade ore bodies by leaching of the primary silica. The nature of this process of enrichment remains a controversial subject. A widely held theory is that ground water, which is a solvent of silica, percolated through the fractures in the taconite, leached out the silica, oxidized the iron, and left in concentration a soft, porous mass of enriched ore lying in linear belts along the outcrop of the Huronian rocks. The heavy pressures on this porous residual ore mass resulted in the sagging or slumping of the formation into the troughlike structures so characteristic of the Mesabi ore beds.

Within the frame of this general formation, the Mesabi deposits divide into three fairly distinct sections. From the extreme eastern end at Birch Lake to the town of Mesaba they are hard and silicious, and much of the iron is finely disseminated magnetite. From Mesaba on for nearly 50 miles to Keewatin they are highly concentrated hematite and limonite. Out of this section has come the stupendous tonnage of direct shipping ore. From Keewatin on west to the end of the range the ore is good, but generally not sufficiently concentrated to be used as it comes up from the pits. It is mixed in with sand, decomposed taconite and taconite. It must be crushed, washed and separated from these foreign materials—"beneficiated"—before it can be sold and used.

Quite by chance the range was broken into by the Merritts and the immediately succeeding explorers right in the center of the soft hematite section where the ore could be scooped up and shipped away. At first it was a simple hand, shovel, team operation. Men shoveled up the few feet of overburden and hauled it over out of the way to the waste dump where more men spread it about. This stripping operation exposed the top of the ore bed. Then with pick and shovel they began to take out the ore. As they dug down into the first operating level, they laid tramways along the incline, extending them as they proceeded on the first terrace. When they had reached the end of the deposit or the land limit of the lease, they opened another terrace on the next lower working level, and carried the tracks along with them.

This hand operation did not last long. The steam shovel had been invented, and it was exactly suited to this kind of service. One was brought into the Virginia mines in the winter of 1894. It weighed 35 tons. It was so heavy that the new D. M. & N. railroad could not haul it during the summer months because the track was not ballasted and could not sustain the weight. It was transported in the dead of winter, and at night, while the frozen ground provided a foundation for the rails. Two narrow-gauge locomotives were also brought in to haul the cars out of the pits. The operators thought they were doing wonderfully well when the new steam shovel stripped off 13,000 yards of overburden during the first month and 14,000 the second. From that time on, the development at these mines was as spectacular as the direction of its evolution was obvious and inevitable. The shovels got bigger and bigger year by year, the engines and cars were enlarged apace, new railroads to the mines were built, more workers arrived on the range and rolled out 31,389,888 gross tons of ore during the first decade of its operation.

Here, indeed, was strong competition for the old companies which had been on the Marquette Range for 40 years and were now going down deeper and deeper underground with expensive machinery to get their ore. And once again high technical efficiency and smart managerial planning were urgently called for.

13

THE PANIC AND THE MERGERS

IT WAS obvious to the Cleveland men, even before the Mesabi was opened, that iron-ore mining was entering on a new era that would demand far-reaching changes in managerial structure and operational techniques. The necessary steps could be undertaken only by the consolidation of the small independent units into organizations large enough to command vastly increased capital resources. These resources would, in turn, permit new efficiencies to lower production costs.

Samuel L. Mather recognized this compulsion in the 1880's. The discovery of the Gogebic and Vermilion deposits and the rapidity with which they were developed in the late 1880's reinforced his conviction and made it plain to others. While the Merritts were still cruising along the Mesabi ridge with a dip needle in search of outcrops of ore, Mather was formulating plans to unite the Cleveland Iron Mining Company with the Iron Cliffs Company, which had adjoining properties on the Marquette Range. While Lon Merritt was lobbying a bill

through the Minnesota legislature to permit him to acquire for a song a prospector's lease on extensive acres on
the Mesabi, Mather was negotiating a merger with Samuel Tilden, Jeptha Wade and others of Iron Cliffs. Just
as the plans for the merger were completed in the autumn
of 1890, about the time the Merritts were sinking their
test pits at Mountain Iron, Samuel L. Mather reached the
end of his distinguished career. He died in Cleveland in
October 1890. His son, William Gwinn Mather, was
called on to succeed him, and in 1891, as the rush to the
Mesabi began, the two companies were formally consolidated to become The Cleveland-Cliffs Iron Company.

The Iron Cliffs Company, one of the older corporations at Marquette, had been organized by Samuel J.
Tilden of New York, William B. Ogden of Chicago, and
other associates, in 1864. Charles T. Harvey, who had
moved to Marquette after building the canal at the Sault,
had interested them in the iron deposits. They bought
38,000 of the valuable acres in Marquette County which
had been granted by the Government to aid the building
of the canal. They were instrumental in building the
branch line of the Chicago & Northwestern Railway from
Negaunee to Escanaba in 1864.

The Iron Cliffs Company was under smart and well-
connected management, and it became the most vigorous
competitor of the older Cleveland Iron Mining Company. Samuel Tilden himself, president and director of
the company, was a successful corporation lawyer and a
political reformer. He had served in the New York legis-

lature, and had been governor of the state. The Democratic Party nominated him for the office of President of the United States in 1876. He received a majority of the popular vote, but was defeated in the electoral college by Mr. Hayes of Ohio. He died in 1886, leaving most of his estate to the Tilden Trust for public benefactions.

William Ogden, born in New York near the capital at Albany, had gone out to Illinois where he became the first mayor of Chicago in 1837. He made a fortune in real estate, and in business as a contractor, paving downtown Chicago streets and lining them with buildings and homes. He operated huge lumber camps in Illinois, Wisconsin and Michigan. He became the first president and director of the Chicago and Northwestern Railroad. His Chicago mansion was destroyed in the great Chicago fire of October 1871, and in forest fires of that same year, he lost his timber and lumber towns. He lost over $2,000,-000 in these fires. He was in New York at the time of the disaster. He rushed out to the scene and remained there until the rebuilding of Chicago and of the lumber town of Peshtigo were well under way. He was a director of Iron Cliffs until the year before his death in 1877.

Several other directors of this company were also men of large affairs. William Henry Barnum, who succeeded Tilden as president and general manager in 1869, and was a director from 1864 to 1885, was a United States Senator from Connecticut, a frequent delegate to the Democratic National Convention, and chairman of the party's national committee when Tilden ran for the Presidency. Abram S. Hewitt, another director, had been mayor of New York City and a Congressman from New York. He was a son-in-law of Peter Cooper, founder of Cooper Union, and head of an important iron company which had supplied General Washington with materiél in the Revolutionary War. Edmund H. Miller, another director, was head of a Wall Street brokerage firm and a member of the Stock Exchange. William L. Wetmore of Marquette was a pioneer iron man of the Upper Peninsula and a partner of Dr. Morgan Hewitt of the Cleveland Iron Mining Company. Seth Baldwin of Escanaba was agent for Iron Cliffs responsible for securing ships and the prompt dispatch of iron-ore cargoes. Edward Cooper, a director from 1876 to 1882, was a brother-in-law of Abram S. Hewitt, and once mayor of New York.

Directed by such a group of successful statesmen with headquarters and powerful connections in New York and the East, Iron Cliffs was, indeed, a formidable rival for the Cleveland company. These executives, being skilled and experienced politicians, knew how to smooth the path and overcome resistance to their objectives. They made an alliance with the Peninsula Railroad, and they outmaneuvered their competitors in many instances in securing low rates and ships to transport their ore to southern ports. Their connection with the Peter Cooper furnaces afforded them an additional and assured outlet in the East for their ore.

Iron Cliffs prospered under such management. It had

acquired in 1867 the stock of Harvey's Pioneer Iron Company. By 1889 it held 55,350 acres of valuable properties. It owned two Pioneer furnaces, with buildings, shops and machinery. It had opened up several mines on the south edge of Negaunee and Ishpeming along the present handsome Cliffs Drive. It had extended the railroad to the Foster Mine and the nearby Iron Cliffs blast furnace. At the time of the merger it owned several good mines, including the Salisbury, Ogden, Foster, Tilden, Holmes, Barnum and Empire, and the huge underground deposit at the Cliffs Shaft in Ishpeming. It was producing around 300,000 tons of ore a year and 25,000 tons of pig iron. It was connected with the Illinois Steel Company, owning 596 shares of its stock.

But time was having a reckoning with these industrial leaders during the difficult transition period in the iron-ore business. The early officers and stockholders were aging and dying and their holdings were passing into other less interested hands. It was an opportune moment to consolidate interests. The merger was effected with the help of Jeptha H. Wade, Sr., a Cleveland man, who had spent some time in New York. He was a director in the Iron Cliffs Company, a friend of the men in the Cleveland Iron Mining Company and a director in this company.

This remarkable man had had a career worthy of the times in which he lived. Thrown on his own resources at an early age by his father's death Wade, at the age of 12, went to work for a tanner and shoemaker in Knowlesville, New York. The following summer he worked in a brick yard at six dollars a month. The next year he was offered an increase to $40 a month as a brick molder; but he accepted his older brother Andrew's offer to learn the carpentry trade. At the age of 16 he was Andrew's foreman. Two years later the boom, which followed the discovery of coal in Pennsylvania, attracted Jeptha and another young man, Enoch Yost, to Pottsville, Pennsylvania. Here the boys made enough money for a trip to New York and Philadelphia, but after seeing the sights of the big towns, Jeptha returned to his birthplace, Seneca Falls, New York, and resumed work with his brother, but this time as a partner. In the autumn of 1831 he left his brother and went to work in a sash and door factory run by Erastus Partridge, a wealthy merchant and banker of the town. Several years later Mr. Partridge took in Mr. Wade as a partner.

Early training brought to the surface the heritage of rare mechanical talent and inventive genius for which Mr. Wade, in later years, was famous. He built and repaired clocks, mended pumps and invented machinery. He also made a flute. As a joke he was asked to build a violin cello; he fashioned one and it was played in the church for several years. He easily learned portrait painting, and made a living at this for a number of years. He helped construct a telegraph line along the Michigan Central Railroad. He invented the Wade Insulator, which is still in use, for telegraph wires; and he made over the telegraph line between Cleveland and Cincinnati from failure to success. He devised an armored cable to carry the wires through the water of the Mississippi, but neglected to apply for a patent. He took over struggling little companies all the way to the Pacific Coast and united them into the Wade Lines; later consolidated with others, these became the Western Union Telegraph Company of which he was president.

He settled in Cleveland in 1867, became a successful banker and president of railroads. He was one of the charter trustees of the Lakeview Cemetery Association and founder of the Cleveland Protestant Orphan Asylum. Shortly before his death, Mr. Wade donated to the city of Cleveland several thousand acres of land to establish a municipal park, which is known as Wade Park, and gave substantial gifts to many charities. He was a friend of Mather, W. J. Gordon and other iron men of Cleveland. He invested in mining stock and out of his rich experience gave able direction for 20 years to the management of the Iron Cliffs Company.

Jeptha Wade was responsible for the merger of this company with the Cleveland company. He bought a majority of the shares of stock in Iron Cliffs. In 1889 he held 14,055 shares out of a total of 20,000 shares of Iron Cliffs stock outstanding. In 1891 practically the entire capital stock of this company was acquired and turned over to the newly formed Cleveland-Cliffs Iron Company. The union of all these interests brought under one management a diversified business and control of the most important and largest mineral lands in the Marquette dis-

HAWKINS MINE, MESABI—RAIL HAULAGE

trict. Its assets were worth more than $6,000,000. The combination placed the new company in a more favorable competitive position in the total picture. In addition it had the advantage of 40 years of experience in mining and transportation. And it also enjoyed the good will and high respect among its customers and other business concerns which the integrity of Mather, Gordon, Wade and their associates had won for it.

W. G. Mather had no doubt of the future, despite the unprecedented extensions of new mining companies along the unfolding deposits around Lake Superior. The situation was summed up in an announcement to the stockholders. This arrangement, it said, "will insure the joint and harmonious working of the contiguous properties of the two constituent companies, and will inure to their advantage in many ways, chiefly in the saving of administrative expenses, in the elimination of competition, in advantage in purchasing supplies and in transactions with railroads and other transportation companies, a large corporation, in these days of consolidations, having more power and influence than a small one. . . . From . . . its other earning and resources a surplus can be accumulated which will enable it to pay a regular quarterly dividend on its stock, thus giving it a stable value in the market, independent of any temporary depression in the iron trade."

The old Jackson Iron Mining Company had struggled along through the years doing a fair business. But as the surface ore was exhausted and mines went deeper, the costs became too great for its capital structure. It was bought in 1887 by Jeptha Wade, Wilson B. and W. M. B. Chisholm, of Cleveland, and Samuel Mitchell of Negaunee. It continued to operate on a small scale under the new management through the 1890's. By that time the consolidated Cleveland-Cliffs was moving forward so well that it decided to add this company to its combination. The merger was completed in 1905 and the historic Jackson Company became a part of Cleveland-Cliffs. Its assets were then just over half a million dollars.

The Cleveland-Cliffs, and later the Jackson, merger was the first and a characteristic example of what soon became the most important development in the business of mining iron ore. This was, indeed, an era of consolidations on a scale never before witnessed in America. Out of the amalgamations emerged a few leading and well-placed companies competent to cope with the new conditions. One of these was organized and developed by William G. Mather's half brother, Samuel.

Samuel was the older son of Samuel Livingston Mather. He was born in Cleveland in 1851. He married a daughter of Amasa Stone, the railroad builder and public benefactor of Cleveland. He had gone out to Ishpeming as a young man to work for his father and learn the iron-ore business. He was badly hurt in a fall in the Cleveland Mine. He had to withdraw from the business and spend some years, part of the time in Europe, recovering from the accident. Finally restored, he re-entered the mining business, as fascinated by it as his brother William. He made many extended trips to the Peninsula during the period of the rapid developments there. For reasons of his own he decided to leave his father's company and form his own partnership.

He may have been prompted by his friendship and admiration for two immensely capable young men whom he had met at Cleveland, Ishpeming and Marquette. One of them was Jay C. Morse, a mining expert. He had been a clerk in a hardware store at Painesville, Ohio. Then he had gone up to the Peninsula as agent for the Cleveland Iron Mining Company. He was also a stockholder in the McComber Iron Company, of which Samuel L. Mather was president, and general agent in charge of operations at the McComber Mine in Negaunee. His name recurs in the official reports on the developments at Marquette as one of the enterprising agents.

The other young man was Colonel James Pickands of Akron, who had earned his title in the Civil War, and was now making his way forward in the business world. He was attracted to Marquette by the vigorous growth which the mines had stimulated there. He also had before him the examples of Peter White, Doctor Hewitt and other men who were making fortunes at Marquette. Peter had started with nothing at all, but he was already in business for himself and on his road to wealth and influence as merchant, banker, real-estate dealer and iron manufacturer, and son-in-law of Doctor Hewitt. And

Hewitt himself was living the good life with his family at Marquette, and was adding to his fortune as he helped build the city.

Colonel Pickands decided to go out to this newest frontier town of opportunity. He got his small savings together, sailed out to Marquette and went into the business of selling coal and hardware. The boom at the port and back on the range created a good market and Pickands' business prospered greatly. He became a good friend of White and Hewitt, and made the acquaintance of Fayette Brown, who was also getting his start and beginning to do big things on the Upper Peninsula. These men were constantly thrown together in the small circle of talent gathered together in this wilderness. They talked a great deal about iron and the future. Pickands and Morse were sure they could make "spiegel" or spotted pig iron from the ore at the McComber Mine, in which Pickands also had bought stock. When they heard that the Munising furnace was to be blown out for repairs, they put 50 tons of their ore on a scow, sailed it over to Munising, and, on their second attempt, made "a beautiful spiegel pig iron."

The spirit and enterprise of these young men attracted Samuel Mather. He first approached Jay Morse with the suggestion that they form a partnership to deal in pig iron, ore and coal. Morse liked the idea and made the further suggestion that they try to interest their friend Colonel Pickands, who was already well along as a prosperous merchant in a related business. They went to see him and laid their proposition before him. He accepted immediately, and the partnership of Pickands, Mather & Company was thus formed in the year 1883.

Mather, Morse and Pickands were joining their interests just as Charlemagne Tower and George Stuntz were driving their railroad back from Two Harbors to Soudan and while new reports on the Vermilion Range ore deposits were circulating daily. With the possible exception of Tower and Stuntz, no one watched the developments in the Minnesota field with more interest than these three ambitious young merchants. Their interest was heightened by the instantaneous success of the Minnesota Company and by their own prosperity. For the new partnership made money and expanded its operation with striking rapidity. Pickands, Mather leased and began to operate mines on the Marquette Range. They also began to acquire their own fleet of freighters. They bought the *V. H. Ketchum*, launched in 1874, the biggest ship of the day, with a 16-foot draft. Too big at the outset for the docks and channels, she became enormously profitable as the channels and facilities were enlarged to accommodate her capacity. She was the beginning of this firm's present Interlake Steamship Company fleet of 35 ships, marked with a narrow orange band near the top of the black funnels. Among their ships are the *Samuel Mather*, the *Col. James Pickands*, the *Jay C. Morse*, the *Amasa Stone*, and the *Fayette Brown*.

This firm also went into the smelting business producing iron at various furnaces, and into coal mining in western Pennsylvania. Four years after the partnership was formed, with the output at Vermilion rising phenomenally, Pickands, Mather decided to get into Minnesota ore. They bought an interest in the Minnesota Exploration Company. From this beginning they expanded through various acquisitions and reorganizations to become one of the largest operators in the Minnesota ranges.

Another of the important companies formed at about the same time with almost identical business interests was that of M. A. Hanna & Company, later to become (1922) The M. A. Hanna Company with offices in the Leader Building at Cleveland. The company had grown out of a pioneering coal business managed by Daniel P. Rhodes of Cleveland. It brought coal from the Youngstown mines over the new canal system to Cleveland. In the 1850's the Hanna family also moved to Cleveland to engage in the wholesale grocery business. They prospered. They extended their operations to the upper lakes, sending up to Marquette supplies of all kinds and bringing back ore. Young Mark Hanna (Marcus Alonzo), growing up in Cleveland, met and married the daughter of Mr. Rhodes. He soon found himself in the family business of buying and selling and shipping. In 1885 the Rhodes firm was reorganized and became M. A. Hanna & Company with a widening interest in charcoal pig iron, furnaces, coal and a fleet of carriers.

Hanna leased mines in the Upper Peninsula. He needed his own ships to carry his ore. He ordered them from the shipbuilding firms, and launched in record time the beginning of the Black Line with the schooners *Genoa* and *Verona*, and the steamers *Geneva* and *Vienna*. The M. A. Hanna Company fleet is now composed of 13 carriers. Like Pickands, Mather, Hanna also invested heavily in the Mesabi ore fields.

These three, Cleveland-Cliffs, Pickands, Mather, and M. A. Hanna, became the dominant independent companies. The Mesabi, for the most part, became linked directly with the mills of U. S. Steel as a basic source of supply under its control. The other ranges were also, to some extent, affected. This great corporation combined the mining and shipping interests of Carnegie and Rockefeller in a series of spectacular developments and mergers which, for a time, caused grave concern among the independent companies. For they brought under the control of this single giant more than half of all the known iron-ore resources in the United States, backed by such vast capital that the small businessman could hardly comprehend the figures.

Rockefeller, as we have indicated, had become involved in mining more through coincidence than through plan. His restless and sagacious mind, stimulated by a huge income, was interested in many things and he saw possibilities in other fields. Though he made many excursions into these opportunities as diverting (and lucrative) bypaths, he never departed too far or too long from his central concern with oil. He left the detail of investment to his agents after he had gained a grasp of the situation and made appraisal of the opportunity. His surplus had become so vast that it had to flow into many enterprises. He himself said in *Random Reminiscences*, "Most of these properties I had not seen, having relied upon the investigations of others respecting their worth."

His reliance on two friends, fellow members of the Fifth Avenue Baptist Church, had first brought him into Lake Superior ore. Colgate Hoyt had known Rockefeller in their Cleveland days when he was coming up in the banking and brokerage business. He became president of the American Steel Barge Company. Charles L. Colby from Boston had lived out in Wisconsin during the feverish developmental days, constructing canals, serving in the legislature, and getting interested in the Gogebic iron ore. The first mine to be opened on the Gogebic was the Colby, at Bessemer, where ore had been discovered in 1880. It was mined by the first steam shovel used in Lake Superior ore fields, and was shipped out of Milwaukee to Cleveland in November 1884. Hoyt and Colby formed a partnership and went into railroad building, real estate and mining. They persuaded Rockefeller to invest with them. During the seven years before he got involved with the Merritt boys he had put money into mines on the newly opened Gogebic Range, including the Aurora and Tilden, two of the richest deposits.

Some of Rockefeller's investments with Hoyt and Colby were not turning out well. He instructed his agent, Frederick T. Gates, formerly a successful Baptist minister and now one of his closest advisers, to look into

the state of these mines. He looked just at the moment
when the Mesabi was firing men's imagination with its
tremendous possibilities. Gates was enthusiastic. Rockefeller was somewhat cautious. He did not rush into the
Mesabi, like the Merritts and others. He almost backed
in, step by step; but once in, and seeing the wide open
road, he could not resist its lure. He went all the way. In
fact he was already there before some of his rivals even
knew he was traveling, and his presence caused them
much concern. He traveled in, as we have already briefly
noted, over the Merritt boys' new railroad.

Through Hoyt, Colby and Wetmore the Merritts
reached Gates. The Merritts, counting their paper investments and their watered stock, already considered themselves multimillionaires. They were wonderful woodsmen, and they looked like the stalwart men they were,
dressed in cowhide field boots, heavy flannel shirts and
Mackinaw pants, and with virile, handle-bar mustaches.
But they were babes in the woods in the difficult matters
of high finance and sound business management. They
made commitments that were wild even in the atmosphere of frenzied speculation characteristic of the early
1880's. When they went East to get capital in the first
days of the Panic of 1893, they traveled in their own
private car and were costumed like a cartoonist's drawing
of a robber baron during the muckrake period. They took
Gates on an inspection trip to Duluth and the Mesabi
in this private car. Their own intense zeal, described by
De Kruif as "maniacal eagerness," infected Gates, though

he knew that their financial position was desperate if not hopeless. "The Merritts," he said, "could not have sold their stocks in the open market . . . for more than half their debts."

Gates summed up the desperation in these vivid sentences:

The Merritts in Duluth had let their contracts for the big dock and for the extensions of the railroad; the contractors were at work with hundreds of men; the railroad debt was piling up at the rate of $10,000 per day; the mines were idle, and no money was forthcoming from the East. The financial arrangements planned in the spring (1893) had completely broken down. The railroad was trembling on the brink of receivership. Interest on the bonds was not paid. Suits were actually begun. There were labor riots on the Missabe range. Contractors were knocked down on the Merritt Railroad by their enraged men. Knives were drawn. Men actually entered the railroad offices in Duluth and demanded cash on their pay checks at the end of drawn revolvers. The personal affairs of the Merritts themselves were in no better shape. Some of their creditors were jumping on them and threatening to sell their collateral.

"Must have some money at once to save the Merritt boys' collateral, which means control of best properties," so Leonidas Merritt wires me in July. The complete financial collapse of the Merritt-Wetmore syndicate, of the Merritts personally, and of the Duluth, Missabe & Northern Railroad is now a mere question of days.

Rockefeller took Gates's recommendation and put up the cash when no other financier was willing or able to invest a cent. Once Rockefeller was in, the demands on him accelerated. He added $500,000 more to keep the railroad going, and continued to advance capital until he had added $1,500,000 more. He granted a personal loan to the Merritts of $150,000 to help them retain their collateral. These steps had led Rockefeller so far that he formed the Lake Superior Consolidated Iron Mines Company in 1893. The Merritts put into this company their equities in the railroad and in five mining companies, and Rockefeller merged into it all his mine stocks and securities. He took as his share in the new company six-per-cent first-mortgage bonds totaling $4,299,000. He made an agreement to buy at the regular market rate all the ore produced that year from the Mountain Iron Mine.

All of this aid proved of no avail to the Merritts in the face of the depressed market of 1893-1895 and the fantastic overextension of their obligations. They failed and crashed, and Rockefeller had to take over with still heavier investments. Even in this state of affairs Rockefeller gave the Merritts a year's option for buying back their stock. Lewis J. Merritt and his son Hulett, still unable to buy, asked for and received from Rockefeller a renewal of their option. In fact he kept on renewing it regularly for seven years, and both Lewis and Hulett became millionaires when the stock was finally sold to U. S. Steel. The others did not repurchase their stock, nor did they renew their options. Instead, Alf, with the aid of a lawyer of doubtful repute, brought suit against Rockefeller which, as we have noted, was finally settled out of court.

Rockefeller now pursued the project on the Mesabi with his customary vigor. He saw the railroad through to completion, got the docks built and put the mines into production. He poured in millions of dollars year after year without taking out any profits from the operations. His Lake Superior Company, capitalized at $30,-000,000, was the biggest and most powerful on the Mesabi. It had the resources to tide it over the Panic and depression years which drove so many smaller and frailer companies to the wall, and to survive the period during which the furnaces were experimenting with and adapting themselves technically to the demands of this fine soft ore that required wholly different treatment from the hard ores to which they were accustomed.

The sagacious Rockefeller quickly saw what the Cleveland-Cliffs Company had seen long before, that ships were the controlling link in this vast business chain from the mines on Lake Superior to the ore ports and mills on Lake Erie. He was quietly surprised that big steel men like Carnegie had not seen the necessity of connecting their steel mills with their source of supply and means of transportation. He had adopted this as a central principle in building his oil empire. It was equally valid for the ore business. Having formed a great ore company and acquired a railroad from the mines to the loading docks, he proceeded to build his own ships.

Rockefeller called in an old, though casual acquaintance, of his Cleveland days, Mr. Samuel Mather, now a business competitor. To his surprise Rockefeller asked him to get 12 new ore carriers built promptly in the Great Lakes shipping yards for the Rockefeller fleet. This, Rockefeller explained, was not really a competitive fleet, because it would carry his own ore, and regardless of what any other company did, he would have his own freighters. Samuel Mather accepted the commission. He got bids from each of the small rival builders for one or two ships, according to their capacity. Each thought it was bidding on the same order. When the bids were all in, every one of them was accepted, and the shipyards went to work to turn out in record time 12 ships of the most advanced design and carrying capacity.

These ships became the great ore-carrying fleet of Rockefeller's Bessemer Steamship Company, with headquarters in Cleveland. Before the wild 1890's were over it was operating 28 freighters capable of bringing down in one season 3,500,000 tons of ore. By 1901, so rapidly was the industry growing, this fleet numbered 60 vessels, and was rivaled only by the Cleveland-Cliffs, the Federal Steel and the Lake Superior Iron Company combined fleets. The loading docks were enlarged and modernized so that a whole train of hopper-bottomed cars could be run out on them and the ore dumped into the hoppers. New efficiencies in loading and operating the vessels were introduced and the cost was lowered. Rockefeller made no attempt to crush or crowd out the other established companies. He followed in this instance his often expressed principle, "I've always tried to make friends with my enemies. I've always said that when your competitors make money you do too; I've never wanted to drive a competitor out of business." This fleet set a new standard on a larger scale which was met by the other companies, and the resources of all were required to supply the increasing market.

Rockefeller's fleet, with the aid of the independents, also carried Carnegie's ore on contract. This arrangement, which could easily squeeze Carnegie, soon became irksome to his proud position. The whole price structure was rising at the turn of the century, and the cost of ore transportation increased. Rockefeller offered Carnegie all his holdings in mines, railroads and steamships in 1899 for $50,000,000. Carnegie turned it down. Rockefeller then bought the McDougall whaleback pig fleet of 30 vessels, leased all the Mitchell boats of Buffalo, and other ships, and these, added to his new Bessemer freighters, gave him a corner on shipping. The Carnegie Company proceeded to build up its own fleet of carriers by forming the Pittsburgh Steamship Company, with offices in the Rockefeller Building in Cleveland, with capital of $5,000,000.

Smaller operators could not survive such heavy and continued burdens. The magnificent Biwabik Mine is a fair example of what happened on the Mesabi Range in these years. It was owned by lumbermen who in turn leased it on a 25 cent royalty to the Biwabik Iron Company. This company subleased it to the Biwabik Ore

Company on a 50 cent royalty, guaranteeing to mine or pay advance royalty on at least 300,000 tons per year and to exhaust the mine in 20 years. It stripped off the overburden with steam shovels at a cost of $90,000. It brought in locomotives, built tracks and purchased general equipment. By that time, with the Panic spreading, and with all these millions of tons of 65 per cent ore lying exposed, it had exhausted its capital and could not raise more. It gave up its contract. The Biwabik Bessemer Company took over and soon ended in bankruptcy. Rockefeller acquired the first lease on a 30 cent royalty and made it a part of Lake Superior Consolidated Mines. The process was repeated over and over again.

The older Minnesota Iron Company was equally active during the depression years and was second only to Consolidated. It bought mines on the eastern edge of the Mesabi which were readily served by its own railroad from Vermilion to Two Harbors. As the small and poorly financed companies went under and defaulted for lack of money, it bought up at cheap prices thousands of acres. In one week in April 1893 it purchased 7,600 acres of ore-bearing land. It conducted systematic explorations in the district and bought, among many other rich properties, the great Canton Mine, for $1.25 per acre. By investing something over $1,000,000 during these ripe years it gained control of about 40,000,000 tons of ore, and options on more than 13,000 acres of land. By owning its own railroad, it was in an independent position at the mines. To gain the same freedom on the lakes it organized in 1887 the Minnesota Steamship Company and built six big new ships to carry its product down the lakes.

Henry W. Oliver followed the same pattern. In the process of trying to assure an independent supply of ore to the steel mills, he ran up against the enormous outlays of capital required to equip, open and put into production the ore mines. He turned to his old Pittsburgh friend Henry Frick, chairman of the Carnegie Company. Frick saw at once that only the largest concerns could handle these operations, and that the potential advantages to the steel interests were immense. Carnegie's protests and objections were vigorous and heated. "Oliver's ore bargain," he said sarcastically, "is just like him—nothing to it. If there is any department of busines which offers no inducement, it is ore. It never has been very profitable, and the Messaba is not the last great deposit that Lake Superior is to reveal."

Carnegie was right, as of 1892, in that the whole venture was a risk. But Frick was convinced of its ultimate certainty, and finally, over Carnegie's objection, went in with Oliver. He put up half a million dollars, received half the stock in Oliver's company and a mortgage on the mines. The capital was invested in further developments. Oliver brought in steam shovels and soon they were scooping up Mesabi ore to be mixed with other high-grade Bessemer ores for the Carnegie furnaces. Oliver-Carnegie leased more mines. Then they formed an alliance with Rockefeller's Consolidated and even leased his Mountain Iron and Rathburn mines. They acquired the

POWER DAM AT DEER LAKE, ISHPEMING

DRAGLINE AND CONVEYOR STRIPPING, CANISTEO MINE

CONVEYOR AND STOCKER, CANISTEO MINE

Pioneer Mine on the Vermilion Range and the Norrie and Tilden on the Gogebic. To get the Norrie they had to buy out 300 stockholders.

This amalgamation of small companies into giants and their apparent combat for control shook the entire industry. They were only preliminary to one more huge and bewildering combination. While Carnegie was threatening to build his own railroads and other facilities, a big tube works at Conneaut, and other plants, the other steel men went to J. P. Morgan to urge him to help organize and finance a merger of their interests. Morgan was agreeable to the proposal, and immediately set in motion his great financial empire to bring it to fruition. He purchased the Carnegie Company for $303,450,000. He brought in Elbert H. Gary's strong and growing Illinois Steel Company and other Chicago properties. But he could not leave out Rockefeller. In one of the most dramatic deals of the age, he swallowed some of his imperious pride and paid Rockefeller's price: $8,500,000 cash for the Bessemer fleet, and $80,000,000 for his Mesabi property, half in common stock and half in preferred of United States Steel.

Rockefeller had been in a position to buy at the right moment on a depressed market, to hold on through a lean period, to bring high efficiency into the total operation from mine to furnace and to sell out when he chose. On the whole, he had done well on the Mesabi.

The U. S. Steel Corporation was formed early in 1901 with capital of almost $1,500,000,000. Its first annual report for the year 1901 showed that the new corporation, through its wholly owned subsidiary, the Oliver Iron Mining Company, owned 65 of the 104 mines which shipped ore that season. It also owned five key railroads and 112 lake vessels which could carry at least two-thirds of the ore required at its mills.

In this manner the pioneering and transitional phase of iron-ore mining was brought to an end and the modern period of big-scale operations inaugurated.

14

MINING BECOMES BIG BUSINESS

The consolidations, highly publicized by the names of Rockefeller, Carnegie and Morgan, caused some anxiety on the part of the American public and their representatives in the Government and the press. Brought up in the era of small private business, they feared the specter of monopoly. They attempted to cope with the potential evil by governmental regulation. The controls which were set up did aid, perhaps, in preventing their worst apprehensions from materializing. Actually the iron-ore industry remained strongly competitive. And under the given conditions, the movement toward a few strong companies was inevitable. By no other means could an industry requiring such heavy financial obligations and such a delicate balance between raw materials and transportation and the processing plants be successfully managed. The mills had to have a guaranteed supply of various grades of ore to keep them running regularly and without interruption. Since the Great Lakes are open to navigation only seven to eight months of the year between the melting of the ice in the spring and the first heavy freeze in the early winter, the mining, shipping and stock-piling of a year's supply must be planned for with close precision.

The amount of capital necessary to sustain such a far flung and expensive operation steadily increased. Even on the Mesabi, where the ore could be scooped up from open pits, the outlay was still great. Consider simply the demand for machinery. In the early open-pit days, when each little company operated a mine or two on slender capital, horses or mules were used as a matter of initial economy. But as the scale of operations enlarged, this form of power became the most expensive and the most wasteful. Major Brooks, writing a classical report in the Geological Survey of Michigan in 1873, said flatly: "If ever there comes a period when our mines do not pay it may be due largely to horses." What he meant was that horses had been introduced when only a little power was needed, and more had been added as the demand increased. Now the mines were involving costs too great to be borne and yet they did not have enough capital to make the transition to steam. At one time 350 horses were employed at the mines, with the expense for all their work reaching $250,000 a year. It cost $650 to work one horse for one year. This investment, Major Brooks pointed out, was "sufficient in itself to supply all the mines in the region with all the additional steam-hoisting and pumping machinery and small locomotives required to do the work now done by horses and at a very much less yearly cost." The day of "pick-and-shovel, hammer-and-drill, horse-and-cart business," he said, was over. He was correct. But the only way the change-over could be effected was by consolidation, because the small operator could stand neither the loss of production during the transition nor provide the capital with which to buy the machinery.

The situation was no different in principle on the Mesabi Range. Little or no blasting or drilling was required. But the overburden had to be stripped off and moved out of the way. Steam shovels were the only practical tools for such massive duty. They, too, cost a lot of money. They had to be manufactured down below, transported to the Upper Lake port, and hauled back to the mines. They broke down frequently and were repaired with difficulty and delay. Steam engines and ore cars were needed for the pits, and the track construction along the cut-away shelves, involving switches at each level, was expensive in material and in labor. Once again, only the strongest companies could engage in this operation, and they needed not one but several mines to make it profitable.

As the competition increased, every penny that went into the cost of a ton of ore became of vital importance. The price of ore declined steadily, driven down by forces outside the control of the individual mine operators. They had to get out more ore at less cost. The only method by which they could accomplish this was a vastly increased capital outlay to provide machinery that would ultimately reduce these costs. Steam and electric power got rid of the horses and increased the output per man in the mines. The power drill could replace the three-man team—one to hold and turn the drill and two to swing the sledge hammers—and it could make a hole more quickly. Machinery could also reduce the burden of all the dead work, i.e., uncovering the ore, or removing dirt and rock and preparing the face for mining. Royalty rates were an important item. They were fixed charges generally covering long terms. Many of them, contracted for during speculative booms, were very high. This was especially true on the Gogebic where some of the properties were saddled with rates up to 75 cents per ton. Oliver had leased Missabe Mountain at what was considered the exorbitant rate of 65 cents per ton, but Rockefeller had secured his at 25 cents.

Every mile of haulage entered into the calculations and the cost. Rail haulage, as compared with water transportation, is exceedingly costly because of the huge outlay for rolling equipment, the relatively small loads on each train, the upkeep of the road and the wages of the men who operate it. Compared to rail costs, shipping by water is cheap, and the distances over which the ore must be transported are great. The water route from Duluth-Superior to Cleveland is 834 miles; from Two Harbors to the same port it is 810 miles; from Ashland, the chief outlet port for the Gogebic Range, it is 789 miles; from Marquette, 598 miles; and from Escanaba, the port for the Menominee mines, 540 miles. The fact that water transportation was available for the shipment of iron ore from these ranges has been of great importance in the development of the Lake Superior district mines. It is even more economical to dump coal out of rail cars into a freighter at Toledo and float the cargo to Detroit than to take the train itself the additional 70 miles overland.

The mines on the Marquette Range, although having the disadvantage of being mostly underground mines as compared to the open pit operations on the Mesabi Range, have the advantage of a short rail haul to the loading docks at Marquette. This, coupled with the lower lake freight rates from Marquette as compared with those from the head of Lake Superior, has served as an offset to the higher costs of underground mining, making possible the continued large movement of ore from this range.

There are other considerations which explain why the immense new discoveries of ore in the basins on the watershed ridge of Mesabi did not stop operations at Marquette and the other ranges. It was true, as Lon Merritt once said, that the ore was so near the surface that "if we had gotten mad and kicked the ground right where we stood we would have thrown up 64 per cent ore, if we had kicked it hard enough to kick off the pine needles." There was no question that it could be mined cheaply and the estimates of 1893 that it could be delivered at Cleveland at much lower rates than Marquette, Gogebic or Vermilion ore, mined under the conditions of that day, were not far wrong. But such great iron men as Andrew

Carnegie and Charles M. Schwab were not just being stubbornly ignorant and blind when they opposed the use of Mesabi ore in their furnaces. "You will find this ore venture," Carnegie said, "like all other ventures in ore, will result in much trouble and less profit than almost any other branch of our business." And Allan Nevins wrote that Schwab told him, "Our experts in the Carnegie Company did not believe in the Missabe ore fields. They thought the ore was poor; that it was not only too fine to work, but too lean, its iron content being smaller than that of the old fields. They ridiculed Rockefeller's investments in the Missabe . . . putting large sums of money into ores that were useless, at least for a long period to come. . . Mr. Carnegie and I wanted to avoid the Missabe range."

The furnaces, of course, were built for hard ores. This soft stuff was like a mass of modeling clay when wet and like dust when dry. In the depression days of the 1890's, when rumor was rife, it was said that carloads of the dry pulverized ore blew away in strong winds and were scattered over the farms of Ohio. It was not a matter of rumor but of fact that when the first charges of this ore were put into furnaces designed for the hard, chunky rock ore, they settled into a heavy mass and then exploded. Furnaces were wrecked and the near-by countryside and buildings were damaged by the hot dust blown out of the furnaces. Law suits actually resulted. It took 15 years for the furnace men to learn how to use these ores except as a small portion in a mixture of other ores. Even then other ores had to be used with Mesabi to "sweeten" them. And since the ores needed to be mixed to achieve the right proportions and specifications, the advantage again went to the larger companies controlling a variety of mines. The ore from any one mine, no matter how high its quality, could not satisfy all the customers. But the company owning several could meet all demands, mixing the ores as desired as they dumped them into the bins at the loading docks.

The mergers, then, were not simply a few big deals dreamed up by financiers and imposed on an unwilling industry. They were the natural means of keeping an industry, vital to the growing nation, strong and productive enough to meet the startling demands on it. William G. Mather, writing in *Proceedings of the Lake Superior Mining Institute*, 1898, summed up the situation in these words:

The Lake Superior mining industry is now in the era of the large corporation or employer, whose organization is as costly as it is efficient; whose fixed expenses are large, and whose aim must therefore be to work regularly, to produce this year as much as, if not more than, last year, so that these fixed charges per ton may not increase, but decrease. The employer cannot now easily reduce his cost when prices and demand are depressed; a complex organization (necessary with a large business) cannot conveniently nor economically be suddenly adapted to a decreased output; men cannot be discharged now and new ones employed later without impairment of system, discipline and efficiency.

We have, then, arrived at this state of affairs: First, low prices and expensive managing organizations, with high fixed charges needing regular and large output; second, a knowledge that the extent of our deposits and future market prospects are of a kind to justify large expenditures for the most efficient plant and best organization.

Assured that it could continue to advance under these conditions, Cleveland-Cliffs proceeded to make the necessary expenditures and the required efficiencies. It had calculated accurately to take advantage of its favorable location. Though the actual mining costs were markedly lower on the Mesabi, they were offset by shorter rail haul and the 40-hour saving in sailing time from the docks at Marquette. The Michigan ore commanded a premium over the Mesabi because of its structure and because it was then necessary as a mixture for the blast furnaces. It was not saddled with such high royalty rates, and the tax structure in Michigan was more favorable than in Minnesota. These considerations, along with the most careful management and development policies, enabled Cleveland-Cliffs to delve deep underground and still stay in business.

The increased strength had come just in time. The iron and steel business, as we have seen, was being dragged down into stagnation by the Panic and the depression of the early 1890's, and at the same time new production problems confronted the new company. One of the most challenging of these was presented at Lake Angeline, a small body of water about a mile long east and west and a third of a mile wide just south of Ishpeming which served as a reservoir for the town's water supply. It was formed by surface drainage from the surrounding hills and emptied into the Carp River. Geologists, attempting to follow the ore deposits, were convinced that a rich mine lay underneath the 41-foot depth of the lake.

Diamond drilling in the winter of 1886 confirmed their opinion and revealed enough ore to justify a heavy investment in shafts and underground equipment. But the mine could not be safely worked without draining the lake, and that meant finding a new water supply for Ishpeming. The water pipes were accordingly moved over to Lake Sally, 80 feet higher in elevation, which gave the town good water with a gravity system and did away with expensive pumping. No substitute was found for the natural beauty of Lake Angeline, which had to give way to the inevitable by-products of an active mine.

The water was pumped out in 1892 and the mine was opened for production on three levels, 100 feet apart vertically. It was an exacting test of mining technique. A crosscut was made from the main shaft. East and west from it the ore body was laid off in alternate pillars and rooms, each 21 feet wide. The ore was then mined in alternate rooms. When a room had been cleared, timbers were erected in the vacant space. The company built a sawmill near the mine for the express purpose of framing timber for the rooms; it was the first mill to be set up to meet this new style of mining. But the ordinary method of "rooming" the deposit would not work because the mud came down into the mine. The caving method was then decided on. They laid out a sublevel at the northwest end of the mine, and dug out a room. Then they blasted together the supporting timbers, bringing in the surface by its own weight. There was enough sand, held back by the timbers, to form a strainer; the water eased through to be pumped out, but the difficult mud was retained. Another slice was then undermined and the process successfully repeated.

This was the mine in which electrically driven trams were first used. The drifts from the shaft into the ore body were so long that it was unprofitable to use men to push the loaded cars. Two motors were installed, capable of drawing a train of ten cars each carrying three and a half tons of ore. The cars were also designed with bottom dumps which were automatically locked as they passed over a bumper between the rails after the load had been discharged into the hopper to be hoisted to the surface by the skip. This mine was ready for active production by the time the ore market revived following the Panic.

Another important question of this transition period was what to do about charcoal furnaces. Cleveland-Cliffs had acquired the Pioneer furnace, but time and the deep depression of the early 1890's had rendered it obsolete. Most of the good charcoal timber in the vicinity had been used up. The market for charcoal iron was falling off in the face of the competition of new processes being developed at the steel mills. Mr. Mather wrote in 1903, "Charcoal is not of course holding its own with coke iron. It cannot be produced as cheaply and the demand for its better quality at the necessarily higher price that must be asked for it, is limited." He was confronting the figures which showed that the peak of charcoal iron production in the United States was reached in 1890 with a gross total of 628,145 tons, almost seven per cent of the total pig iron. Michigan had made 230,796 tons of this total. In 1900 production had fallen to 339,874 tons, just two and a half per cent of the total, of which Michigan had contributed 163,712 tons—almost one half. Despite the falling production, charcoal iron was still a big business, and Michigan was in the forefront of it.

The company decided to build two new modern furnaces. It chose for one of them the location at Gladstone, which we have mentioned, a few miles up the bay north of Escanaba. Gladstone was a new town, founded in 1887 as a deep-water port on Lake Michigan for grain shipments from the West, served by the Soo Line from Minneapolis. It was adjacent to good timber lands and to the mines. Work was rushed along on the new furnace, charcoal kilns and a chemical plant to utilize the by-products. Branch railroads were laid back into the timber lands to serve the logging operations. The furnace had a capacity of 110 tons daily. It continued in operation until 1922 when the supply of wood in this region was exhausted. In 1933, when a new and greater depression finally closed out a gradually dying industry, it was pulled down and sold for scrap.

The other furnace of the same capacity, known as Pioneer No. 2, was located in Marquette. It was especially designed in order to make full use of the by-products in an allied chemical industry. It was put in blast in 1903. In August of that year Mr. Mather took a party from the Lake Superior Mining Institute aboard a train "of six Pullman sleepers and five private cars" from Ishpeming to inspect the new plant, and to visit Munising and Grand Island. In the *Proceedings* this observation was recorded:

To say that this plant is the most modern of its kind in existence, does not convey an adequate idea of the skill with which the best features known to the industry have been brought together, to serve in their several capacities, the perfect working of a harmonious whole.

The site was considered ideal because of the railroad service from the timber lands and the mines and the fine harbor at Marquette for the outgoing product. "The ores," the report noted, "which in this climate would become frozen and unmanageable by long transportation, are received warm from the mines." The track system, it continued, is so arranged "that all raw material comes to the plant from the north; works through the plant from west to east, and the products go out at the south end without conflicting with other traffic. The main arteries of traffic from the north, separate into no less than twelve tracks, which assume grades best suited to their respective functions, and so completely fill the requirements of transportation, that only three cart horses and a truck team are used on the place."

The charcoal kilns, 86 of them, were arranged in two double rows with railroad trestles alongside so that the trains coming in from the timber lands could be switched to the point of consumption to avoid rehandling in the furnace yard. With this method one man could handle 32 cords, or 144,000 pounds per day. When the wood was carbonized, it was forked into buggies, and hauled by an electric engine through the stockhouse and over the scales to the furnace skip. Mixed with ore and limestone, it was hoisted on an automatic skip to the top of the furnace for the charge. "A single operator," said the report, "at a furnace of this class handles something like 300 tons daily, and replaces a swarm of bottom fillers, which are found on the stockhouse floors of all other charcoal furnaces throughout the country."

The boilers were heated by the gases recovered from the furnace, supplemented by the use of bituminous coal. Electric power came from a Westinghouse generating outfit, and water from Lake Superior. Because of the unpredictable condition of the anchor ice in the harbor, the 30-inch water pipe was extended a third of a mile out into the lake. Water was brought into a steel cistern 20 feet in diameter and 30 feet deep, with a stand pipe 14 feet in diameter and 95 feet high to equalize the pressure.

Gases from the kilns were captured and passed through 57 condensers. The liquids then went through 40 odd stills for the production of refined wood alcohol and gray acetate of lime.

The visitors' report concluded with these observations:

The scrupulous neatness with which all departments are kept, received much favorable comment on the part of the visitors. . . . Outside of the working plant proper, we were much interested to note the completeness and practical utility of many necessary accessories, such as the well appointed machine shop, locomotive house, supply house, stables, warehouses, underground water supply and fire protection, and a beautifully equipped office building, where the workings of all departments are kept in an elaborate and most admirable system of accounting.

By combining the manufacture of charcoal iron with the chemical plant, the cost was brought down to the place where it could be sold at a smaller premium over ordinary coke iron and was able to remain in the competition. This pig iron was made of pure wood charcoal and high-quality ore, smelted under low temperature and low blast pressure. Its structure was fine and dense, and it had great strength and unusual flexibility. It was particularly adapted to the manufacture of chilled rolls. When combined with other foundry mixtures, it added little to the cost but much to the quality. It was used for products requiring a chilled surface to give added strength, finish and hard resistance in crushers, grinding belts, dies, cylinder blocks, valves and other high-grade castings.

The draining of Lake Angeline and investment in mining equipment, and the venture into the furnace business were both rather bold management decisions under the conditions of the day. They were based on the carefully calculated future, not on the temporary depression. They made the assumption that Mesabi would supplement and not supplant the older ranges, and that these outlays of capital, which temporarily taxed the resources of this company, would pay dividends in due course under diligent and thoughtful management. The calculations were correct. And they led to still other plans and enterprises which further broadened the scope of the operations.

15

TRANSPORTATION AND FOREST
INDUSTRIES

TRANSPORTATION of the ore has always been a problem second in importance only to the process of digging it out of the ground and hoisting it to the surface. We have noted the struggle of the early days to get the ore down to the docks, first by sled in winter, then by plank road, by mule-drawn tramcars on strap rails, and finally by steam railroad. The cars grew larger and the locomotives became more powerful as the decades passed by and the volume increased. About the same time that Rockefeller was taking over the Merritts' crude railroad and developing it to serve the Mesabi Range, Cleveland-Cliffs projected its own new and modern road from Ishpeming to Presque Isle, the fine harbor bordering Marquette on the north. Joining with the Pittsburgh and Lake Angeline Iron Company, it located and built the Lake Superior & Ishpeming Railway between these two points, a distance of 20 miles. It was completed in 1896. In addition to the main line, there were nine miles of sidetracks and seven miles of leased road, making a total of 36 miles over difficult terrain.

The road climbs up the escarpment from Presque Isle Harbor through a countryside of unusual beauty. The ascent is rather constant, with grades of 1.63 per cent. The longest grade is eight miles through second-growth timber and jutting rock outcroppings. The curves are easy and smooth. Portions of the route seem as wild as on the day when Burt's surveyors tramped along the township lines. Deer and occasionally a bear come out of the woods to the tracks and lift their heads to watch the trains roll by. The long trestle high over the Dead River gorge commands a striking view of the river below and the undulating hills and forests of the surrounding region. But despite its great natural beauty, this is a utility road dedicated to the prosaic work of hauling ore from the mines to the dock. The passenger trains which formerly carried hundreds of people back and forth have been almost entirely supplanted by the highways and the motor cars. The little stations along the way are virtually deserted.

The first shipments of ore came down over the new railroad in August 1896, and by the end of the year 290,-000 tons had been moved to the dock. During 1897, the first full year of operation, 1,036,000 tons went down over its tracks. Four locomotives hauled the cars, and ten more were used for switching service. The cars, 400 in number, were made of wood with center dumps, and held about 30 tons. One locomotive could handle a train of 30 cars, or

900 tons of ore. It brought the cars to a new dock at Presque Isle.

This dock was another of the big investments which had to be undertaken in these disturbed days of the 1890's. Built in 1896, it incorporated all the latest improvements of the period and was projected to meet future as well as present needs. It extended out into the harbor a distance of 1,200 feet. It was 54 feet high and divided into 200 pockets, each holding 160 tons. Its total storage capacity was 32,000 tons, or about a dozen cargoes for the ships of the 1890's, and two or three loads for those of the present day. It proved adequate for only 15 years. By that time it was obsolete and was requiring costly repairs.

The new concrete dock was completed in 1912 and was the first of its kind on the Great Lakes. The foundation was made of wooden piles strong enough to bear the enormous weight of the structure. These were enclosed by a 12-inch timber sheet plank wall, cut off six inches below the low water level and filled with sand to insure a permanent foundation. The dock is the same length as the old one and has the same number of pockets. But it is 54 feet wide and 75 feet high and can store 50,000 tons of ore. The spouts from the pockets are 43 feet above low water and they are 39 feet long. They are raised and lowered for loading operations by electric motors, each motor lifting or lowering six spouts by means of a line shaft.

The ships to be served had in 1912 reached a width of

60 feet. In the meantime many vessels have been widened to 70 and projected to 75 feet. The long spouts, however, designed with foresight, are able to serve the new ships efficiently, and the dock can load 5,000,000 tons of ore in a season. The time saved by these loading methods is really tremendous. At the turn of the century the average turn-around time of vessels at the docks per 1,000 tons was 331 minutes; at present it is 37 minutes. The average tonnage per cargo was 2,881 tons; at present it is 9,465. Fifty years ago the turn-around time, including loading a cargo of the present average size, would have been 52.5 hours; today it is 5.6 hours. This includes time pumping out water ballasts, which in some large vessels requires four hours, time battening down hatches and tarpaulins, and time spent waiting turn at the ore dock. Some loadings take longer because certain cargoes contain more plastic ore than others, and hence the ore does not flow freely. The actual loading time proper of vessels is approximately 3½ hours. The largest single cargo taken from the dock was 16,558 gross tons. The largest number of vessels loaded in a single season was 608 in 1941, and the longest loading season was 253 days in the critical war year of 1942. The 2,816-foot-long breakwater, completed in 1939, protects the harbor.

The equipment on the railroad and the improvements of the road bed and tracks have kept pace with the loading demands at the dock. The little locomotives became big steam engines, and these in turn are already giving place to the more powerful and more economical Diesels which can pull over a third more load with a 40-per-cent saving in fuel costs. The size of the trains is determined by the steep grades to the west. Two of these Diesels can pull 110 empty steel cars from Marquette up to Ishpeming and bring down 5,900 gross tons of ore each trip. That is a 555-per-cent increase over the train loads of the first season. To accommodate the increased weight the old wooden trestles over the gorges have been replaced with modern steel structures.

At the mines, of course, the branch tracks run off from the main line to the various stock piles. The ore is dumped directly into the cars or loaded from the stock piles by power shovels. These operations are scattered over the active range. But down at Presque Isle the yards are extensive, crowded and very busy. Switch engines break up the trains, pull the 50 to 70-ton cars across the scales for weighing, and shunt them off to separate tracks according to the nature and quality of the ore they contain. The weather gets cold around Marquette before the shipping season is over. As early as November 10 the thermometer frequently falls to ten degrees. Since the soft ores contain from 10 to 13 per cent moisture, they often freeze during these cold snaps and have to be thawed out, both in the cars and in the dock, to be handled. Fifty-six cars at a time are run into a special ore-thawing house which is heated by steam to about 120 degrees. It sometimes requires eight hours to thaw out a load, and, of course, runs up the cost of shipping.

The loaded ore cars are assembled according to ore

classification to fill specific orders. They are then shoved up the mile-long approach to the dock on a grade of one and a half per cent, and over a four-track steel trestle 600 feet long which connects with the dock. Here they are placed above the designated pockets and dumped. The big freighter comes alongside, the motors lower the spouts, and out pours the cargo into the hold.

The steel plants require ores of varying analyses, but they do not have stockyard space to store them separately. Many of the ore cargoes are, therefore, composed of ore taken from several mines and mixed in the dock into a single grade of specified analysis. As the ore is loaded into railroad cars at the mines a representative sample is obtained of each five-car lot (the "knotted rope method") and these samples are immediately sent to the laboratory to be analyzed.

The ore grader is advised of the time of arrival and the tonnage required for each vessel. The analytical results of the five-car lot samples are also forwarded to him. Having this information available, he selects in varying proportions ores from the different mines amounting in total to the tonnage required for each vessel so that when mixed the average analysis will closely approximate the published analysis of the specified shipping grade. Identification of the cars included in this group and the name of the vessel for which it is intended is forwarded to the dock office. As these cars arrive at the dock yards they are placed in a group, or "blocked out," and then hauled to the dock. Each dock pocket holds five cars. No two cars from any one mine are dumped consecutively into the same pocket. Thus the process of mixing continues until each pocket is filled. As each pocket is opened and the ore flows down into the vessel hold, the five cars of ore become well mixed, and, as pocket after pocket is dumped, further mixing takes place.

In the hold of the vessel the ores from the various mines have lost their identity in this mixing process and are now a single grade of ore of uniform quality, meeting the analytical specifications required by the steel companies for burdening their furnaces.

It is no small undertaking to keep in repair 30 steam engines, three Diesels, 2,620 freight cars and all the trackage. Near the switch yards, set in spacious grounds that are as neat as a park and look like one, is a modern railroad shop with a 20-stall enginehouse, a turntable, a blacksmith shop and a locomotive repair shop, a powerhouse, a storehouse, a coaling plant, a storage tank for Diesel fuel oil, lumber yard, and everything else necessary for the repair and maintenance of a Class 1 railroad which must be self-contained and self-sustaining on the Upper Peninsula of Michigan.

This decision of the mid-1890's to finance and build its own railroad soon led Cleveland-Cliffs into other related activities. We have already observed how intimately the forests were connected with the mines. Houses had to be built for the miners, quantities of timber were needed for the drifts underground, and the chemical plants with their charcoal kilns ate up logs by the acre.

The mining and timber businesses were inseparable parts of a single operation. All through the merger period the strengthened companies were adding to their holdings. Cleveland-Cliffs purchased half the stock of the Arctic Iron Company with interests in mining properties near Negaunee which were inactive. It acquired an interest in the Lake Superior Iron Company, the Regent Iron Company and the Imperial Mine at Michigamme. These mines, having been idle, had filled up with water and had to be drained. It also acquired the Carp River furnace, and two tracts of land in the vicinity of Marquette, the 40 acres known as the Agricultural Lands—where it built the Pioneer furnace No. 2—and an excellent tract of 17,000 acres of hardwood forest at Sauk's Head Point, northwest of Marquette.

Shortly thereafter, in 1900, it also purchased the Munising Railway together with about 84,000 acres of hardwood timber lands and the picturesque Grand Island lying in Lake Superior just off Munising and within sight of the Pictured Rocks. Munising (Indian word for "place of the big island") had long attracted the attention of the white men, just as it had invited the Ojibway Indians centuries before. The wooded hills circle it on three sides, and it faces the island which protects it from the open sweep of Lake Superior to form its small but excellent harbor. In the 1850's, while Marquette was booming, some land speculators mapped out a town on paper and tried to promote settlement. Their scheme died during the Civil War. It came to life, on a different pattern, during the period of charcoal furnaces at Munising from 1868 to 1877, and then retrogressed. It did not revive until 1895. Some sawmills were then built to supply the heavy market for lumber and a tannery was also erected there. The railroad was constructed that same year to service the lumbering operations and to give an outlet from Munising to Little Lake, a distance of 37 miles through solid forests of pine, hemlock and hardwood, where it connected with the Chicago & Northwestern Railway between Negaunee and Escanaba.

William G. Mather watched this development with great interest. He was particularly fond of the region for its natural beauty and of Grand Island for its historical interest and its natural state. He also observed that this remarkable stand of timber in such a favorable location was precisely what was needed to supply the Cleveland-Cliffs mines and the new furnaces and chemical plants. The company bought the railway, including the town site of Munising, in 1900. Two years later it built the Marquette & Southeastern Railway to connect its Lake Superior & Ishpeming road with the Munising line. The railway ran from Marquette to Lawson, a distance of 27 miles, and completed the opening up of the timber lands. Later extensions and consolidations brought the main line to 102 miles. Including all its branches it has a total of 262 miles of track serving the mines and forest products.

Mather took his guests from the Lake Superior Mining Institute at Ishpeming over this newly opened railway system in 1903. After stopping to inspect the furnace at

Marquette, the party again boarded the special train. The minutes of the Institute carry a good account of the journey which recreates the scene of 50 years ago.

The ride along the shore of the beautiful bay was indeed an enjoyable feature of the trip. In order to save time a lunch was provided on the train. . . . The trip over the Marquette & Southeastern and Munising Railways, a distance of 52 miles through a magnificent timber belt and newly developed farm lands, was a surprise to many who had never before traveled over this new road. The operations of the Pioneer Iron Co. on their several wood jobs along the line of these roads, gave the visitors some idea of the magnitude of the charcoal feature of the furnace industry. Here were seen thousands of cords of the finest hardwood ready for shipment to the kilns at Marquette. At Chatham, on the line of the Munising Railway, is located the State Experimental Farm.

Arriving at Munising at 2 o'clock P.M., the party proceeded to Beach Inn. . . . Launches had been provided to take the visitors across the bay to Grand Island, Munising Falls and the Pictured Rocks. The distance from Munising to William's Landing, on Grand Island, is about four miles and to see a dozen launches crossing the bay at one time, was indeed a very pretty sight. The water in the bay was calm and good speed was made. The party were shown the several points of interest and about three hours were very pleasantly spent. The Island is eight miles long by about four miles wide and contains over 13,000 acres. It is almost wholly covered with a dense growth of a variety of hard and soft woods. The island is owned by The Cleveland-Cliffs Iron Co., who are doing much to improve it as a forest preserve and to protect the native game which was prey for the hunter heretofore. They have also added other animals such as moose, elk, antelope and several species of deer, all of which are said to thrive in their new home. At William's landing can be seen the remains of an old trading post with the line of the stockade which was built by the first settlers some sixty years or more ago for protection against the Indians.

A few of the more timid members of the party who did not take the lake ride, paid a visit to the buildings in course of erection for the paper mills of the Munising Paper Co., situated in the western part of the village.

After supper, which was served at Beach Inn, the party was directed to Alger County's new and beautiful court house, where the evening session was held.

This 1903 description is substantially accurate a half century later. The party would now motor over modern concrete state highway M28 around the gracefully curving bay and along the south shore of the lake instead of going down to Lawson. They would cross Laughing Whitefish River and see the white-capped breakers roll in on the clean sand beach at Au Train. They would still dine at Beach Inn looking out on the bay. And they would go by launch across to Grand Island. They would still find it covered with the same virgin timber, except for the natural wastage from storms, lightning and windfalls; they would still see the remains of the old American Fur Company trading post, and some of them could spend

the night in the cottage of Abraham Williams, a native
of Vermont, who chose this spot for his home and Indian
trading post in the middle years of the nineteenth century. It is one of 16 cottages which, along with the big
white Williams Hotel, afford summer vacation accommodations on the edge of the forest fronting the bay and
the city of Munising. A rustic road winds all the way
around the island, sometimes plunging through the green
tunnels formed by the forest, then bursting out on a
rocky headland overlooking the sweep of the lake, and
in spots along the northeast shore commanding magnificent views of the red and yellow Cambrian sandstone
Pictured Rocks on the Peninsula shore east of Munising.
It is one of the few spots remaining in the region where
one may in our time experience the sensation of a forest
primeval, the constant high rustling of the leaves, the
soft light on the cool, damp forest floor, the wild deer
loping through the ferns.

With the development of the charcoal furnaces at
Gladstone and Marquette, its interest in paper mills and
the acquisition of timber lands and reserves of approximately 750,000 acres, the company went in for logging
on a vast scale. It did not wastefully operate the forest,
cutting out certain of the more profitable species, as many
of the big lumbering companies in Michigan, Wisconsin
and Minnesota did. It went about the business scientifi-
cally, as it did with the ore mines, utilizing all the forest
products, and, quite early in the process, instituted re-

searches and planned cutting programs to guarantee the future of this renewable resource. The logging industry, carried out on this plan, led naturally to still other industrial plans. The maple, birch, oak, ash and other veneer logs, cream of the forest products, were sorted and sent to the Great Lakes Veneer Company, acquired in part by Cleveland-Cliffs in 1912 and named The Munising Veneer Company. In this plant the wood was reduced to thin single-ply veneers for the interior finish of buildings, for doors, furniture, airplanes, etc. The northern Michigan birch veneers are considered the finest in the world.

The next lower grade of birch and maple went to the Munising Woodenware Company, organized in 1911 for the manufacture of bowls, rolling pins, butter molds, spoons and other household articles. Beech logs were made into clothespins in another department. Other saw logs were hauled into the sawmills to be made into lumber. Spruce, balsam and hemlock pulpwood went to the Munising Paper Company, constructed in 1902, for the production of wrapping paper. Later on a bleach plant was built to produce high-grade bond papers. The cedar was cut up into ties, posts, poles and shingles. Many of the sound hardwood trees were cut for use in the company's mines. The hemlock bark went to the tannery. Everything else, including the logs decayed at the heart, was sawed up into appropriate length and shipped to the kilns for the furnaces and chemical plants.

To handle this big operation a Land and Lumbering

Department had to be organized. It was set up in 1896 with headquarters at Negaunee. The constant acquisitions extended the company's timber lands in a belt irregularly distributed along the south shore of Lake Superior covering roughly the north half of the central portion of the Upper Peninsula. The lands reached eastward from Marquette County 175 miles to Sault Ste. Marie. The Land and Lumbering Department was instrumental in the early days in organizing the Northern Forest Protective Association, made up of the principal large timber owners on the Peninsula, to patrol the timber area. It carried on extensive educational campaigns for fire prevention to help conserve this important natural resource. The general public have always had the feeling that the land belongs to them and that they have an inalienable right to hunt and fish where they please. The Association accepted this premise and actually encouraged hunters and fishermen by issuing camping leases at nominal rentals to enlist their aid and encourage public interest in conservation and the prevention of fires. Its efforts led directly to the present efficient fire prevention system under the State Department of Conservation.

During the 1920's the production of all these logging operations averaged about 22,500,000 feet each year, or 8,000 carloads. That meant the cutting of nine acres of virgin timber every day. It took 300 men, 100 horses, two locomotives, four power loaders and two tractors, working in four or five logging camps, to get out this quantity of timber. Forty-eight miles of railroad track were required in the operation, and each year 15 miles of it had to be lifted and relaid in another part of the forest. The company discontinued its own logging operations in 1938, sold its equipment, and turned the work over to independent contractors. Its own technical foresters, however, check and supervise all cutting on the lands. The operations are more extensive than ever. With modern power saws and motorized equipment, the output during World War II reached up to 75,000,000 board feet per year.

Timber cutting of such magnitude called for earnest study of conservation to assure maximum use of the present stand and to provide for its renewal. The first tentative step was taken about 1900. A forester was hired to make experimental plantings in cutover areas for "reforestation," and to study the growth of timber. Another and longer step was taken in 1942 with the introduction of scientific forest management. Dr. Henry S. Graves, nationally known forestry expert from Yale University, was engaged as consultant to make a careful survey of all the timber lands of the company and recommend a program to perpetuate the standing timber, and at the same time provide an ample supply of logs for its mines. A major portion of the company's present holdings of about 300,000 acres was set aside for forestry purposes and the plan of selective cutting was introduced. This management plan is based on a cutting cycle of from 20 to 25 years. About one half of the merchantable timber in the

Photograph by Henry Mayer

MODERN SHAFT MINE, MATHER "A," NEGAUNEE

SPOTLESS HOIST ROOM, MATHER "A"

present stand is selected for cutting. It is taken out skill-fully, leaving the other half free for continued growth. About 75,000 acres were logged in this manner from 1942 to 1949. The entire area will have been selectively cut by the end of the first cycle, and the process may begin again on the new crop.

Anyone who has seen the bleak and barren remains of a forest after total cutting, and has then inspected a like region after the loggers have finished their supervised selective logging operation, will feel heartened and en-couraged by the advancement that has been made. Along one main logging road that goes through 17 miles of solid selectively cut hardwood forests, where the cutting was done in 1942, one must look closely to find any stumps or other evidence of logging. The smaller trees left stand-ing, responding to new living space, have shown amazing growth, and a permanent yield of timber seems to be assured under the present Forest Management Program.

Cleveland-Cliffs also engaged in active co-operation with the Government to establish the Upper Peninsula Forest Experiment Station at Dukes, in Marquette Coun-ty. It donated to the Government a section of land which was later increased by purchase to 5,000 acres to study methods of logging northern hardwood, to determine the most satisfactory type of cutting, and how to improve the productivity of cutover lands. It cleared 240 acres near Rumely for an experimental farm to demonstrate the fertility of the soil in that district, and encouraged Belgians to come into the region and farm it. It sold land on easy terms covering long periods of time to induce farmers to settle and cultivate the land. Other large acreages, not adapted to agriculture, were disposed of to the State and Federal Government for state and national parks.

$$\boxed{16}$$

A NEW ERA IN UNDERGROUND MINING

IRON-ORE mines are not renewable resources. When a deposit has been exhausted, it must be replaced by discovering a new one. That process has been going on, at considerable expense, for more than half a century. Cleveland-Cliffs, looking forward to long-range operations, began to acquire additional mines in 1902 to keep pace with the huge investments and expansions in railroads, timber lands and equipment of all kinds. In that year it leased its first mine—the Crosby—on the Mesabi and acquired the Maas property in the city of Negaunee. A little distance to the southeast was the Negaunee Mine, which had been opened and operated on a small scale by Captain Samuel Mitchell in 1887. It was leased to the Negaunee Mine Company in 1904, but operated by Cleveland-Cliffs under contract. The purchase of the Jackson Iron Company in 1905 further rounded out the mineral properties of the company in the Negaunee-Ishpeming district.

The Athens Mine, adjoining the Negaunee on the south, was discovered in 1905 by diamond drilling. It is operated by Cleveland-Cliffs, though jointly owned by the Dalton Ore Company. It was held in reserve and was not opened until 1917. It was brought into production in 1918 during the closing months of World War I. On west of Ishpeming, in what is known as the North Lake district of the range, another rich deposit was located in 1907. Three shafts were sunk into the ore body and the extensive Morris and Lloyd mines were developed.

Meanwhile, beginning also in 1902, a drilling program was started in the Gwinn district, 18 miles south of Marquette. Some small operations had been carried on there at the Princeton and Stegmiller mines, but the full extent of the deposits was unknown. The drilling revealed enough ore to warrant the opening of additional mines, and one by one the Austin, Stephenson, Francis, Gwinn and Gardner-Mackinaw mines were placed in production. In 1905 the company purchased the Princeton. It connected these properties with the Munising & Marquette Railroad.

This Gwinn district became celebrated as a model community. The town of Gwinn, with a present population of around 1,300, was named for William Gwinn Mather's mother. It was planned under the personal direction of Mr. Mather. From his earliest days with his father's company, right on through his own presidency, he had taken a keen interest in the health and happiness of the miners and their families. Long before it was common to do so, and at a time when it was not a popular policy to pursue, Mather had been a pioneer in welfare programs.

Since labor accounted for 70 per cent of the total cost of iron ore on cars at the mine, Mr. Mather reasoned, even if the employer were not a humanitarian (as Mather certainly was) it would behoove him to provide conditions to promote "good health, intelligence, contentment and industry" and to prevent "sickness, accidents, ignorance and restlessness."

Relief and pension funds, health service, good housing, workingmen's life insurance associations, co-operative distributive stores, schools of all kinds, schemes of recreation, etc., have been fostered in a wonderful degree by some employers, principally in Europe, to further the good and prevent the bad conditions . . .

The opening of the Gwinn district offered Cleveland-Cliffs the opportunity to plan and build the community from the beginning. It was laid out on the east branch of the Escanaba River by Warren H. Manning, a prominent Boston landscape architect. The company prepared the site, built streets and sewers and constructed a hotel, a bank, some stores and other buildings. Lots were sold at cost to employees who might wish to build their own homes. For others it erected neat houses and sold them, also at cost, on long-term arrangements to the men who wanted to buy. It built a hospital for community use and employed a visiting nurse to help look after the health of the families. It donated land for gardens, encouraged landscaping, and aided in the building of a handsome high school in spacious grounds. Mr. Mather, as a token of his own interest and generosity, built a clubhouse, equipped with recreational facilities, for all the employees, and a fine outdoor swimming pool was constructed near by which was maintained and supervised by the clubhouse force. These grounds and the pool were taken over later by Marquette County as one of its county parks. Similar clubhouses and hospitals were built in other mining communities.

The lease on the Gwinn Mine was given up in the early 1920's, the ore at the Austin, Stephenson and Francis mines was exhausted, and the Princeton Mine, having reached the point of sharply diminishing returns, was abandoned in 1946. But during the active period of these operations the town of Gwinn provided a happy environment and the tradition of its community life has lived on.

Meanwhile the development of the new mines at Ishpeming and Negaunee was going rapidly forward. The Maas, Negaunee and Athens mines are contiguous properties, all in the eastern part of the city of Negaunee. The workings of the Maas and the Negaunee mines turned out to be in the same ore body, the one on the north and the other on the south side of a wide trough pitching westward on a slight angle. The ore is soft hematite varying in hardness and quality. The Athens is also soft hematite but of slightly different structure from the Maas-Negaunee. Each of the three mines has been oper-

ated as a separate unit with its own shaft and surface
equipment, but all of them are interconnected underground at the main levels for ventilation and safety. The
Negaunee Mine was exhausted in 1950.

Next to the irregular line of hills that frames the city,
the most characteristic objects on the landscape are the
shaft houses and the surface equipment of the mines.
The steel headframes, enclosed for better working conditions during the winter months, rise up 100 feet or more
above the ground. They are a kind of industrial spire
rooted deep in the earth through solid rock beside the ore
body and towering above the timber yards, stock piles,
enginehouse and other buildings clustered about their
bases. The timber yard of each mine is from two to four
acres in extent. It is connected with the shaft by a concrete tunnel in order that the timber and other supplies
may be moved directly from the yard to the shaft and
lowered on the man-cage to the workings below. This
tunnel also has a covered connection with the dry house,
where the underground men change their clothes as they
go into and come up from the mines, and with the shop
buildings where the equipment is repaired.

Out from each shaft generally runs a steel trestle from
35 to 48 feet high. It is supported by reinforced concrete
columns spaced 114 feet apart. During the winter months
when the lakes are closed to shipping by the ice, the ore
comes up in the skips, slides down through a chute into
tramcars of the same capacity, and is hauled out over the
trestle by an endless rope system and dumped on the

stock pile where, in the spring, a giant power shovel will load it into railroad cars for shipment.

The ore is taken out by several methods of mining, depending on the characteristics of the ore and the surrounding rock. Production from the underground mines in 1949 was approximately 10 per cent by top-slicing, 35 per cent by sublevel caving and sublevel stoping, and 20 per cent by block-caving. The block-caving method, reintroduced in Michigan in 1947 by Cleveland-Cliffs, is least expensive, but its use is restricted to ore bodies or areas where ore heights are sufficient to justify the somewhat higher preparatory costs of heavily timbered drifts and raises that must withstand the great pressure induced by controlled drawing of the caved ore.

It is difficult, perhaps, for one who has not actually seen miners at work underground to gain a clear picture of the method of operation by a description in words. The process, however, is fairly simple. After the great shafts have been driven down deep into the earth, main tunnels are cut back in the footwall below the ore body. Each tunnel is from 100 to 200 feet lower than the one above it. Electric-powered trains run through them and they are lighted by electricity. From the footwall tunnel crosscuts are driven across the ore body at 150-foot intervals on each main haulage level. From each of these crosscuts, two-compartment openings, known as "raises," are driven upward at an angle of 65 degrees to the sublevels in the ore body above.

This plan, combined with prior exploration and knowledge of geological features, blocks out the ore for adaptation of the most suitable mining method. Top-slicing may be chosen for clean recovery of a small area under slabby cap rock by extracting 12-foot layers one after another, from the top down, each with its timbered slicing drifts. This method may then be changed to subcaving to reduce timber costs by "slicing" every other layer and caving the ones between. Or, if the overlying rock will arch and support itself across a narrow ore body, open sublevel stoping is employed with consequent higher production per miner because little or no timber is necessary. Finally block caving may be used where ore heights of 100 feet or more are encountered.

As the ore is mined it is moved by an electric scraper to the mouth of the raise. It slides down a chute into cars in the crosscut below. An electric trolley locomotive pulls the cars over a 30-inch gauge track through the main level haulage tunnels. The cars are automatically dumped at the shaft, and the ore flows through a chute to the skip to be hoisted to the surface. To keep the air fresh and circulating throughout the mines huge electric fans force a constant flow down the shaft, and through a series of doors, send it to all the main and sublevels. At the Maas Mine the fan provides 100,000 cubic feet of air per minute.

The water is collected into sumps in the mines and pumped out. The Maas Mine pumps about 1,000 gallons per minute direct to the surface 1,400 feet above. There was a large amount of water at the Athens Mine when it was first developed, but in later years the quantity greatly diminished to only 325 gallons per minute. This is pumped in one direct lift from the tenth level 2,400 feet to the surface.

The increasing depth and mechanization of the mines placed new demands on the source of power. The hydro-electric system begun in the early days of the century was extended. The Hoist Dam and Plant on the Dead River north of Negaunee was put into service in 1916. This was followed by the McClure Dam and Plant farther down the river toward Marquette. The combined output of these two units was 35,000,000 kilowatt hours per year. The Hoist Dam impounds some 2,000,000,000 cubic feet of water, which is sufficient to run the Hoist and McClure stations for one year. The water backs up the valley for 14 miles and covers about 4,000 acres.

By 1929 all the sources of water power within the region had been developed and transmitted by lines on steel towers to the mines and towns. The reservoirs, like glacial lakes behind the high concrete dams, became a picturesque part of the landscape. The power houses, located some distance below the dams, tucked in a spot carved out of the wilderness and landscaped along the stream, are models of neatness in their isolation. All their output is insufficient to supply all the growing needs, and drought years cut down their power. A Diesel electric plant has been built to supplement the hydroelectric installations. A new steam turbo-electric plant was built at Ishpeming and the first unit went into operation early in 1950 to provide additional power for the mines and the region. We observe with interest that the condensing water for this plant is pumped over the hill from old Lake Angeline, which was allowed to refill its former basin after the ore beneath it had been mined out.

The work at the Morris and Lloyd mines in the North Lake district paralleled that at Negaunee and Ishpeming. The Morris was later leased by Inland Steel Company. Some ten miles to the southwest was the Republic Mine of which we have spoken. Opened in 1870, it had been producing steadily a high grade of ore, some of it 68 per cent pure iron. It was acquired by Cleveland-Cliffs in 1914 and operated until the available ore was exhausted in 1928.

In addition to the underground mines there was one open pit on the Marquette Range known as the Tilden Mine. It is three miles south of Ishpeming and is reached by the Cliffs Drive scenic highway. The ore body is exposed on the south side of the hill which rises 180 feet above the level of the swamp. It is hard silicious hematite low in moisture. Much of the overburden is sand and boulders varying in depth from two to six feet. Stripping of this shallow covering was begun in May 1928 by hydraulic methods. A dam was built south of the hillside to impound enough water during the spring thaws to wash away the overburden. Powerful pumps force the water through a six-inch pipe line to the top of the hill, where it is sprayed through a nozzle under great pressure.

The ore, which is hard and tough, has a face of 100

feet or more, and is worked in two benches. Holes are
drilled down below the pit floor about 15 feet apart and
from 25 to 35 feet back, charged with 17-pound cartridges
of gelatin dynamite, and blasted. The heaviest blast in
the pit used 80 tons of dynamite and broke nearly 250,000
tons of ore into chunks ready to be fed into the crusher
and prepared for shipment. The Lake Superior & Ishpeming Railroad built a spur track from the Northwestern
line to the pit to haul out the ore. There is a change
house for the men at the pit, but they live at Ishpeming
and motor back and forth over the Cliffs Drive.

The ore on the Menominee Range was rapidly exploited after it was discovered in the late 1870's. The
situation was somewhat different, however, on the Marquette Range. As the known and more easily accessible
ore was exhausted, the search for reserves was continued
with increasing vigor. For the accumulating knowledge
of the geology of this region indicated that the deposits
were much deeper and more extensive than the earlier
studies had predicted.

We remember that attention was first attracted to this
region by the outcroppings of iron ore at Iron Mountain
and Cleveland Mountain, and that other ore bodies were
discovered gradually as the mining operations proceeded.
Since this whole area had been heavily glaciated and the
iron formations had been covered over and in places
buried deep, the most careful scientific explorations were
necessary to locate and define them.

Disclosure of these facts came slowly—and at great expense. The forecast of Cleveland-Cliffs which persuaded the company to undertake the tremendous new obligations of the 1890's proved to be accurate. The huge demands of the nation for ore during the expansive years after the turn of the century were continued and increased by the demands of World War I; and these in turn were enhanced by the boom which carried the country forward during the 1920's. The market sagged during the years of the long depression of the 1930's, just as it had in the early 1890's, but nearly 30 years of high production had depleted the reserves at several of the best mines to the point where their replacement had to be planned for.

This problem was not so serious on the Mesabi, as we shall see, because test drilling was relatively simple there where the deposits lay near the surface and the range was more clearly defined. It was a very complex problem on the Marquette where the deposits lay deep underground in ill-defined convolutions and pockets and where staggering sums had to be invested before the first ton of ore could be raised to the surface. Accurate calculations had to be made as to the extent of the deposit, the quality of the ore, and the economics of its extraction. A large-scale campaign of diamond drilling was begun in 1937. The purpose was twofold: to find immediate replacements for the mines nearing exhaustion, and to learn more about the geological structure of the region. Were there more comparatively shallow deposits of high-grade ore to be had, or would the shafts in the future have to be driven down deeper and deeper?

Diamond-drill towers were anchored on the northeast border of Ishpeming. The drills cut their way down through the earth, sand and solid rock and found good ore at depths greater than any of the previous mining operations had reached. The drills were moved farther east within the limits of the city of Negaunee. Again they went down and struck ore at depths of from 2,000 to 3,500 feet below the surface. The existence of ore at depths ranging from 2,100 to 2,800 feet below the surface in this neighborhood had been revealed in 1912-1913. Further explorations in 1943 and afterward showed that the geological structures along the strike of the formation between Negaunee and Ishpeming, about two square miles, were favorable. While this discovery was being made, it became apparent that the Negaunee Mine, the company's biggest producer (1,106,694 tons in 1942), was limited because its ore body dipped across the boundary into the neighboring Maas Mine.

The operations in the Maas-Negaunee district were already reaching the settled outskirts of Negaunee in 1907-1908. Although the ore was overlaid with 400 feet of jasper and more than 100 feet of sand, slow caving in of the surface would inevitably follow when the ore was removed. The value of the ore, however, was sufficient to warrant the extraordinary measure of transplanting this portion of the town. A cemetery was moved to a handsome new location farther east. A railroad that crossed over the area to be mined was relocated farther south, away from the ore body. The Marquette highway was detoured round the property into Main Street. The houses were taken north and set up on new and attractive sites. Twenty years later another removal had to be made as the miners pursued underground the lay of the ore body.

The caved-in areas have become a feature of the region. They are all fenced in and abandoned because their surface use is negligible. They break or sag in from the edges. Some of the older ones are stable enough to permit cows to graze in them. Children are trained to avoid them. In places it is necessary for a highway to pass over them; along the western extension of Iron Street the road crosses the old Jackson pits on a fill retained by concrete walls.

With the ultimate exhaustion of the Negaunee Mine in sight, Cleveland-Cliffs followed up the discoveries of their drilling campaign with plans to sink shafts into the Mather Mine property along the ridge between Negaunee and Ishpeming south of Teal Lake. We observe with keen historical interest that the monument, described at the beginning of Chapter Two, locating the site of the first discovery of iron ore on Lake Superior, is almost in the center of this new mining location. Burt and Everett, as well as Marji-Gesick, would have thought it fantastic if some magician had suggested that a century after their discoveries men would be mining ore 4,000 feet below the surface at the spot where they were then standing.

The decision to develop the Mather Mine at such great depths was comparable in boldness in 1940 to the resolutions for expansions made in the 1890's. Millions of dollars and months of labor would have to be expended before any ore would reach the surface. Utilizing all the experience accumulated in nearly a hundred years, and making use of all the advances in machine design and mining techniques, Cleveland-Cliffs proceeded in September 1940 to prepare the location for production. In partnership with Bethlehem Steel, a customer for the ore, it designed a surface layout and located a shaft in an open rolling field east of Ishpeming. Mining men from all over the world have come here to inspect and admire the plant.

The buildings are joined together to form three sides of a hollow square, with the towering headframe standing apart on the open end. The adjoining office building contains a big map room where every detail of the operation above and below ground is carefully charted. The glistening engine room containing the cage and skip hoists with all kinds of signals and indicators looks like a ballroom ready for a reception. The compressors and boiler room are in the corner of the building next to the hoists, and the various shops, oil storage, warehouse,

THE FLEET ICEBOUND IN WHITEFISH BAY

garage and change rooms for the shopmen are in one wing.

The other wing, 260 feet long and 60 feet wide, is for the miners. When we read the accounts of the early cousin jacks at the mines—their houses shaken by the blasts, the men in work clothes climbing down into the pits or being lowered in buckets, with candles for light, and returning red and begrimed to their homes at the end of the day—when we contrast these circumstances with the facilities at the Mather, we are reawakened to the fact of progress in welfare and human concern during the past generation. The miners drive to work in their own cars and leave them in the parking lot. They change from their street clothes in their clean-clothes locker room of the change house. They put on the uniform of the underground crew: long underwear, heavy wool socks, overalls, rubber boots and hard helmet. From the neat and well-ventilated dirty-clothes room, which has 618 racks, they go to the lamp room where an attendant has inspected the batteries and prepared the lamps for their use. They strap the batteries around their waists and clamp a brilliant light to their helmets. They go on down the ramp through the service tunnel to the shaft, where they summon the cage as though it were an elevator in a skyscraper about to whisk them to some floor below. It stops at the level of operation according to signal. And when the miners return to the surface at the end of the day's shift, they remove their work clothes, go to the spacious shower room, wash away the ore stains, and dress again for the street.

The mine underground is a world of its own, and the men who have worked there know every inch of the intricate tunneling on every level, feel at ease and at home there, and prefer it to the work on the unpredictable surface. The temperature is cool and uniform. The giant fans keep the atmosphere fresh as an air-conditioned room. The engine room and pumping system, deep in the pit, is as complete and spotless as the house above ground, and one would never suspect as he walks through it that it is a vast cave hollowed out of the rock instead of a brick house surrounded by lawns and softened by shrubbery.

The drifts are lighted by electricity like a city street at night, and electric trolley locomotives roll through them hauling train loads of ore on the automatic dump cars. The main level and drifts are supported by a new form of timbering. Since underground operation on such an immense scale requires thousands of supports, and since the timbers, even when specially treated, have a short life and must be regularly replaced with new ones, experiments were made to find some material better suited to the conditions below. The Mather drifts exhibit the answer. Special steel frames are set up at intervals from the floor to the ceiling and across the roof, and concrete slabs, like sawed planks, are laid behind them on the sides and across them on top to form a solid protective covering.

Teams of miners, frequently father and son, go along a drift and crosscut, mount a ladder to the particular area which they are working, and loosen the soft red ore under a production incentive plan called "contract work." After they have performed their unique labors, the rest of the process is done by machinery. The electric scrapers drag the ore to the chute and drop it into the cars on the level below. The cars automatically dump their burden into the hopper at the shaft, and the skip hoists it to the surface. The steel headframe at Mather "A" is 197 feet high. The big cylindrical drums in the engine room, eight feet long and 12 feet in diameter, can wind the 5,000 feet of heavy steel ropes which lift the skips at a rate of 2,400 feet per minute. And the skip, plus its load of ore, weighs 38,880 pounds. The ore is dumped from the skip into railroad loading bins built into the headframe, or into the stock-pile cars to be taken across the steel trestle and dumped for future shipment. The yearly output from this mine already has equaled the records set by the Negaunee, and is expected to reach 1,500,000 tons.

The shaft of Mather "A" faces across the open, contoured fields between Ishpeming and Negaunee toward a new and similar shaft and surface buildings on a hill where Mather "B" is being developed. Work on the immense shaft was begun in 1947 and completed late in 1949 to a depth of nearly 3,100 feet. When it gets into full production, the combined capacity of these two Mather operations is expected to be 3,000,000 tons a year, or about 75 per cent as great as that of all ten of the Cleveland-Cliffs Marquette mines in 1929.

Meanwhile the study of the geology and the search for ore goes forward on the range. The company took over from Republic Steel in 1943 its single operation on the Marquette Range at the Cambria Jackson Mine in Negaunee and added it to its unit of properties in this district. With the diamond drills it has moved on westward in trace of the ore formation in the hope of finding a replacement for the Lloyd Mine, which will be depleted within the next several years. Ore has been discovered, but again at depths of from 3,000 to 4,000 feet—from 1,000 to 2,000 feet deeper than the operating levels of the mines to be replaced.

This raises a problem of far-reaching importance which can only be solved by exacting scientific study and creative ingenuity. There are extensive deposits of low grade iron ore near the surface in this region which could be dug by one of the big new electric shovels. The thin ore seams are, in places, of high quality, but are mixed with lower grade bands, chert, or other impurities. Can this ore be separated from the waste material and be concentrated and agglomerated into pellets for shipping at a price competitive with direct-shipping ore mined underground and hoisted 3,000 or 4,000 feet through a shaft sunk through solid rock and operated by very expensive machinery? To get the answer to this question, Cleveland-Cliffs built in Ishpeming in 1949 a new and fully equipped metallurgical and research laboratory where experiments in beneficiation are underway by a trained staff of scientists. In anticipation of a practical economic and workable solution to the problem, the company has explored by diamond drilling since 1947 three possible beneficiation areas of promise in Marquette County.

17

WELFARE AND REORGANIZATION

THE recent developments at the mines, and others that
are being planned, project far into the future the continued life and prosperity of the Lake Superior district.
The outlook is reflected in the faces and the spirit of the
people of towns like Ishpeming and Negaunee. Some of
the miners go from the pits to their own lots, which they
have purchased from the company, to build with their
own hands attractive houses for their families. Second
and third generation sons, educated at the local high
schools and trained in mining by practical experience
and at a college or a university, hold important technical
and supervisory positions at the mines. They take a deep
personal interest and pride in the operations and quite
properly feel themselves an important part of a common
enterprise.

The welfare and safety programs have gone forward
alongside the technological developments at the mines.
The experiment begun at Gwinn was extended with·
heartening results to other mining areas. Through the

first years of the present century William Gwinn Mather spent a good portion of each year in the Marquette district. He maintained a cottage at Ishpeming and one on Grand Island and made himself a part of the civic life of the Upper Peninsula. He saw to it that good houses at very low rentals were provided for the men and he encouraged those who wished to own their own homes to buy or build them. Reflecting his strong conviction that beautiful surroundings contribute to pride in workmanship, he awarded annual prizes for the best-kept homes and gardens. Company land was donated for a new and thoroughly modern 60-bed hospital erected at Ishpeming in 1918. Owned by Cleveland-Cliffs, it is run in co-operation with the Inland Steel Company, the Jones & Laughlin Ore Company, the Oliver Mining Company and the Hercules Powder Company, with special rates for company employees. The company, co-operating with local people, also built a beautiful modern hotel at Ishpeming in 1931, named the Mather Inn.

Through the years a thoughtfully planned safety program has been nurtured at the mines. All during the early days the annual reports recorded a fairly high rate of accidents. Miners, like other people, tend to grow careless through their very familiarity with hazards. They fell off ladders, they were struck by falling rock, they smashed fingers and broke bones. Some of the accidents were fatal. Unmitigated disasters have been few. One of these occurred on the Cuyuna Range, the last one to be discovered in this area, which lies to the south-

west of the Mesabi. It is a relatively small range of
deep mines reaching down into rich veins of man-
ganese ore which was opened up in 1911. To the
north of the Milford shaft was a small shallow lake with
a bottom of sand. It was frozen deep in February 1924.
One afternoon, while the men were working in the drifts
below, this sand bottom caved in and the water from the
lake rushed like an avalanche into the mine. People on
the surface could hear and feel the rumble. Within a
few minutes the drifts and tunnels were filled with water.
Seven men, by luck and superhuman feats, managed to
climb a ladder ahead of the rising tide and reach safety;
41 others were trapped and drowned.

A similar tragedy befell the Barnes-Hecker Mine near
Ishpeming two years later. Before attempting operations
at the mine, the company had taken every precaution to
insure safety. Both the State Geologist and the Inspector
of Mines for the State of Michigan had inspected the
mine. The lake above the known ore body had been
drained and ditches dug to carry away any surface water
that accumulated in the bed. Nonetheless, through the
mysterious movement of waters underground, a flood
broke through into the mine and filled the shaft to a
depth of 815 feet. One miner, who climbed from the
second level to the surface, survived. Fifty-one others
were caught by the in-rushing waters. Operation at the
mine ceased and the shaft was sealed.

Such disasters are rare, and almost in the nature of acts
of God like earthquakes, tidal waves and flash floods. Like

Photograph by James E. Munger

UNLOADING ORE FROM THE WILLIAM G. MATHER AT ERIE, PA.

HOMEWARD BOUND

the daily crashes on the nation's highways, it is the accumulation of accidents which might have been prevented that causes greatest concern. The companies have worked diligently on this problem. Incongruously, one of the obstacles to success was a certain apathy on the part of some of the workmen. Posters and slogans are helpful, but by themselves they are not effective. The companies have added a program of training workers to do their jobs carefully and alertly and to make a habit of production with safety in all operations. The potential hazards of each step of the work are noted and analyzed in advance, and the protective steps to offset them are made a part of normal procedure. The accident rate is going down.

The companies took the initiative in the campaign for safety. Cleveland-Cliffs back in 1911 formalized its program, on which it had been working for many years, by organizing a Safety Department and creating the position of Director of Safety. It was among the first to do so. A Central Safety Committee was formed to include top management, superintendents and heads of departments. They drew up standards of safety rules and safe practices and published them, and placed them in the hands of every employee. They solicit suggestions for revisions, and recognition is given to the mines with the best safety records. A banner safety flag flies at the mine which has worked longest without an accident.

The Safety Department keeps a close check on all operations. It inspects both active and idle mines, checks ventilation and dust, fire hazards and fire-fighting equipment, and it receives regular reports on hoisting ropes, mine hoists, cage and skips, cage safety catches, slack rope alarms, shafts, ladderways, shaft stations, airways, fire patrols, fire extinguishers and first aid, water hydrants and hoses and every detail of the complicated machinery of mining. The men must wear hard toe shoes and hard helmets, respirators in any dusty places, and safety eyeglasses where there is any danger of flying chips. Drilling through hard ore and rock is done with water-fed drill machines, and when rock is blasted, all dust and gases are knocked down with water blasts. The blasted material is also soaked with water and kept wet throughout the operation. At certain locations a fine mist of water makes a curtain through which the air must pass to be relieved of any harmful dust. Mine rescue and first-aid training is conducted for selected men by three members of the Safety Department who hold U. S. Bureau of Mines Instructors' Certificates. In addition the company maintains a Central Mine Rescue Station at the Negaunee Mine, and has erected a new one at Mather "B." The Lake Superior Mines Safety Council, which began its meetings in 1919, holds an annual conference, usually at Duluth, to consider new ways and means for the prevention of accidents and to keep abreast of the changing conditions at the mines.

The welfare program has gone hand in hand with the practice of safety. When William Gwinn Mather took over his responsibilities there were no safety, welfare or industrial hygiene departments at the mines, no fixed provision for the injured or the sick, or for those too old to labor. He took an active interest in these matters, first as a pioneering and a personal concern, and then in 1905 by creating a special Welfare Department. It carried into effect many of the suggestions which he had made before the Lake Superior Mining Institute back in 1898 regarding the necessity for providing financial help "in sickness and death, and for medical treatment," for good housing at low rents and with good sanitary arrangements, for improving health conditions in the mines, and for increasing and extending the educational opportunities for the miners and their families. He expressed his own sense of responsibility in a concluding sentence:

I would not like to close, however, without bearing witness to the feeling that upon us who have been more favored by education and opportunity for attaining success in the struggle of life than has been vouchsafed to many of our employees, there rests that obligation so well expressed by the words "Noblesse oblige."

Mather's vision has been largely realized. In addition to the broad program of housing, education and medical attention already noted, a pension system was put into effect in 1909 to care for the men at the age of 65 who had worked for the company for 25 years or more. This was terminated during the depression of the 1930's and retirement allowances substituted. A new pension plan was instituted in 1949 to supplement the income from Social Security payments. An attorney and counsel of Cleveland-Cliffs became a member of the Governor's Commission to draft the original Michigan Workmen's Compensation Act of 1912. An Industrial Hygiene Department was also created in 1939 which gives physical examinations to all employees and carries on a follow-up program for their continued health and well-being. A few years later group life, health, accident and hospitalization insurance was made available to all employees. Indeed, the present-day towns on the iron-ore ranges, with their alert and healthy citizens, and with their churches, schools, Y.M.C.A.'s, hospitals, clubs, summer cottages, rest cottages, parks, recreational grounds, flower gardens, window boxes, shrubbery and vines, and tree-lined streets, bear witness to the human achievements which match the technical advancements in the iron-ore mines.

While the company was carrying forward all these developments in the mining district, it was also undergoing a critical and demanding reorganization within its corporate body. The industry, as is plain from the story which we have seen unfolding, has passed through a series of cycles, each presenting problems of exacting difficulty. In broad outline, there have been three of these cycles dramatic in character. The first, of course, was the pioneering period in which a few gifted and capable men organized small companies, went into the wilds of the

Upper Peninsula and, by herculean efforts, brought a few mines into active and profitable production. The second was the stern and rigorous period of the late 1880's and the 1890's during which deep mining was begun on a large scale and the ore pits of the Mesabi were uncovered, bringing with it by necessity the mergers and reorganizations which we have noted. The pattern thereby established held with few alterations throughout the first quarter of the twentieth century during which production of iron ore reached new high levels.

A third cycle was introduced by the boom of the 1920's and the devastating depression which followed the crash of 1929. The most optimistic predictions of 1900 about the future of iron and steel were modest indeed in the face of the actual facts of industrial expansion during the period of the Coolidge prosperity. As General Poe, who designed the Poe Lock at the Sault in 1896, once said with much wisdom about shipping on the Great Lakes, "The wildest expectations of one year seem absurdly tame the next." During this era of mass production in the automotive, radio and kindred industries, competition had grown keener and keener as the years passed, and certain adjustments were made necessary. Producing plants and various types of business began to acquire fabrication divisions and also their own sources of raw material. Some of the smaller steel companies found it wise to have an assured supply of raw material, and for this purpose made connections with the producers of iron ore.

At this point Cyrus Stephen Eaton, a Cleveland investment banker, evolved a plan for consolidating a number of steel plants into one big and self-contained enterprise. It seemed like a natural thing to do in 1929, a year of great business activity. The two giant steel corporations were U. S. Steel and Bethlehem, which Schwab had built into U. S. Steel's biggest competitor. If Eaton could bring a group of the smaller independent concerns into one big organization, he would create a third corporation second in size only to U. S. Steel. The Republic Iron and Steel Company provided a structure around which to build. To it would be added Trumbull Steel Company, Trumbull-Cliffs Furnace Company, Steel and Tubes, Incorporated, Union Drawn Steel Company, Bourne-Fuller Company, Berger Manufacturing Company, Central Alloy Steel, Donner Steel Company, Inland Steel, and Youngstown Sheet & Tube. This amalgamation would be named the Midwest Steel Company, with headquarters and control in Cleveland. It would be able to effect economies which could not be accomplished by the separate companies operating independently.

For their assured source of iron ore it was contemplated that they turn to Cleveland-Cliffs. Its large holdings of ore properties, both active and in reserve, and its 80-year record of thrifty management, conservative in operation but progressive in employee relations and technical improvements, made it a most desirable ally to complete the unit. Cleveland-Cliffs also had investments of its own in several of the independent steel companies to which it sold iron ore. It had bought some of the stock outright, and some it had taken in lieu of cash payment for ore during periods of financial stringency through the course of the years.

William Gwinn Mather had gone out to California for the winter. He agreed to discuss the plan with Mr. Eaton if he cared to come to Pasadena. Mr. Eaton went out, and after four days of conference they negotiated an agreement which was approved by the Board and became known in the trade as the "Pasadena Pact." Shareholders of Cleveland-Cliffs voted to create in the capital of The Cleveland-Cliffs Iron Company an issue of 500,-000 no-par shares of preferred stock paying cumulative dividends at the rate of $5.00 per year which was distributed to the holders of common stock on the basis of 1¼ shares of the new preferred stock for each share of common. In addition, a special cash dividend of $5.00 per share was declared and paid to the holders of common stock.

A new corporation known as Cliffs Corporation was organized in May 1929. It had a capital structure of 800,-000 no-par shares, approximately 400,000 shares of which were exchanged, share for share, for the common stock of Cleveland-Cliffs. An equal number of shares was issued to Mr. Eaton and his associated companies on the deposit of certain shares of stocks in steel corporations, having a market value of approximately $40,000,000. When the transaction was completed, the Cliffs Corporation, in addition to owning all the common stock of Cleveland-Cliffs, owned stock of Republic, Inland,

Youngstown Sheet & Tube, Central Alloy and Wheeling Steel.

This proposed combination naturally aroused great interest and provoked rivalries. Just as the plans for merging Youngstown Sheet & Tube with Republic were ready to be consummated, another group of steel and raw-material men, anxious to prevent this merger, developed a plan to merge Youngstown Sheet & Tube with Bethlehem Steel. It looked for a time as though this latter arrangement would go through. But Mr. Eaton, when the Midwest plan appeared about to collapse or be seriously injured, brought an injunction suit to stop the merger. The result was a long, bitter proxy fight and expensive legal battle fought in the Youngstown court. The newspapers of the day were filled with stories about it and the leading personalities involved. At the end of the prolonged fight, the merger with Bethlehem was blocked. But the merger of Youngstown Sheet & Tube with the other companies was also blocked, and the plans for a third steel empire had to be abandoned. The other steel companies in the proposed merger, excepting Youngstown Sheet & Tube and Inland Steel, ultimately were consolidated with Republic Steel.

In March 1930, as the depression deepened but while hope was still alive that the corner would soon be turned, Cleveland-Cliffs, carrying out a commitment previously made, acquired a majority interest in the stock of the Corrigan-McKinney Steel Company. This company owned a modern group of blast furnaces, coke ovens and steel works in a desirable site in Cleveland, and some valuable iron-ore mines in the Lake Superior region. The transaction was entirely a Cleveland-Cliffs matter. The purchase was made while the Youngstown battle was still being waged.

Although the injunction suit blocking the Bethlehem-Youngstown merger was successful, and interest in the Midwest project had begun to cool, Cleveland-Cliffs management resolved that the logical disposition to make of the Corrigan-McKinney investment was to offer it to the Republic Steel Corporation. Because of the favorable location of the Corrigan-McKinney plants, it appeared a wise move to combine this plant with the other plants of Republic, which would enable Republic Steel to compete more readily with markets west of Youngstown. At this juncture the president of Republic, Mr. E. T. McCleary, died suddenly of influenza, and while Mr. Girdler, chairman of the board of Republic, was engrossed with management problems, the gloom of the depression deepened throughout the nation. The market for ore dropped off and virtually ceased, and most of the companies had to consider ways and means of keeping alive. Cleveland-Cliffs was faced with the enormous burden of carrying charges arising out of the collateral loans given to purchase the Corrigan-McKinney stock. The years 1931, 1932, 1933 slowly passed. In each year plans were projected to dispose of the Corrigan-McKinney investment, but were unsuccessful. The national economy struck bottom in collapse with the bank holiday in February 1933, and the tragic bank failures which attended and followed it,

Without its long and honorable background and sound business structure and the confidence of financial leaders, Cleveland-Cliffs would have been in the hands of receivers, or trustees, like so many other firms of the day. Instead, a Bankers Advisory Committee was organized in 1932 from among the four Cleveland and the four New York and Chicago creditor banks, under the chairmanship of Harris Creech, president of the Cleveland Trust Company. Mr. Creech, handicapped by a recurrent illness, called on Mr. Edward B. Greene, who was chairman of the Executive Officers Committee of the Cleveland Trust Company and also a director of Cleveland-Cliffs, to aid him in this work. The prolonged depression and the resulting banking crisis made necessary the continuing function of the Bankers Committee. The position of Cleveland-Cliffs was made worse by the liquidation of the Guardian Trust and the Union Trust companies of Cleveland, in which it had maintained a large portion of its cash deposits.

In this situation Mr. Mather determined that the company would be greatly benefited if its affairs could be under the active direction of a banker who combined long financial experience with an intimate knowledge of the company's business. With the full endorsement of the Bankers Committee, he prevailed on Mr. Greene to assume the presidency of Cleveland-Cliffs in 1933, with Mr. Mather becoming chairman of the board of directors. It was a happy choice. Mr. Greene was born in Cleveland in 1878, graduated from Yale in 1900, and served as trustee of Yale University from 1925 to 1947. Immediately after leaving college he joined the Cleveland Trust Company where he served with distinction in many capacities from 1900 to 1933, and as chairman of the Executive Officers Committee until 1949. He married Helen Wade of Cleveland, the great-granddaughter of Jeptha H. Wade, Sr. Her father, J. H. Wade, Jr., was president of the Citizens Saving and Loan Company and for many years vice president and director of Cleveland-Cliffs. In 1932 Mr. Greene, with six other leading citizens, was appointed by Governor George White to form the Emergency State Bank Committee which served until the Ohio State Legislature created the State Banking Advisory Board. He was reappointed the following year for a three-year term. The recodification of the state banking laws prepared by this committee was adopted by the legislature. He is a past president of the Cleveland Chamber of Commerce, and in 1940 was awarded the Cleveland medal for distinguished public service. He had had close and friendly relations—personal and family—with the Mathers.

Disregarding personal preference Mr. Greene accepted the appointment as president on September 1, 1933. His calm and assured manner in those rough days, his understanding of finance and his personal acquaintance among the bankers of the nation inspired the loaning banks with confidence. A probable receivership was avoided and Mr.

Greene, with careful deliberation, went about the business of funding the large obligations of the company and began the process of reducing the heavy financial burden.

Mr. Greene was rather fully occupied with the financial and banking problems during his first year with the company. He needed able executive assistance in the handling of actual operations and sales. With admirable judgment he called on Alexander Cushing Brown. Mr. Brown belonged to a family that had distinguished itself through three generations, as we have noted earlier, by its contributions to the development of the Great Lakes. One of his grandfathers, General James Barnett, had served as a director of the Cleveland Iron Mining Company in 1861-1862, and from 1866 to 1878; and the other had been manager of the Jackson Iron Company. His father had invented the Brown hoist. Mr. Brown was born in Cleveland in 1885 and graduated from Yale in 1907. He joined his father's company as machinist in 1909, and in 1916 became vice president and general manager of the company, now known as the Industrial Brownhoist Corporation. In 1925 he was made president of the corporation. His intimate experience gained while working in the shops, coupled with his natural human inclinations, developed in him a deep interest in labor relations. During his presidency of the Cleveland Chamber of Commerce in 1921-1922 he devoted much of his effort in this direction, particularly in the building trades.

Mr. Brown joined Cleveland-Cliffs in September 1934

as vice president. In April 1947 Mr. Greene was made chairman of the board and chief executive officer, and Alexander C. Brown became president of the company. Tall, distinguished, with a touch of whimsical humor that often relaxes overly tense situations, he has continued the enlightened industrial-relations policies begun some 60 years ago by William Gwinn Mather. The results of the co-ordinated work of Mr. Greene and Mr. Brown, together with their efficient organization, have been exhibited in the story of the new round of developments at the mines. It was a period corresponding in a new and still larger way to that of the 1890's. The reorganization was effected in time for Cleveland-Cliffs to meet with full strength the great demands that were placed upon the iron-ore companies at the close of the 1930's and in the unprecedented days during and after World War II.

18

LATER DEVELOPMENTS ON THE MESABI

Up on the Mesabi Range the developments, though quite different from those at the underground mines, were equally spectacular in their way. Instead of the great shafts reaching deep under the surface and the drifts honeycombing the ore bodies, steam shovels were stripping off thousands of acres of overburden and laying bare millions of tons of ore in the open pits. As the mergers stabilized the operating companies, and as the demand for ore rose steadily through the twentieth century, mine after mine was opened all along the range. The Oliver Iron Mining Company, subsidiary of U. S. Steel, was the largest of the organizations, but the M. A. Hanna Company, Pickands, Mather & Company, Jones & Laughlin's Inter-State Iron Company, Republic Steel Corporation and Inland Steel Company, as well as many other concerns, acquired extensive holdings and operate mines throughout the area. The Cleveland-Cliffs Iron Company, because of its confidence and commitments in the Marquette district, did not enter the Mesabi on a large scale until World War I. It had, however, leased property on this range in the expansive period of 1902. It had conducted some explorations and had purchased and opened the Crosby Mine both as an open pit and an underground working. In 1919 and the years following, its holdings were increased and it became an important producer of Mesabi ore.

In sheer tonnage, of course, the Mesabi mines far surpass the combined output of all the other ranges. In the great peak year of 1942, when the total shipments of the Lake Superior district iron ore reached 93,495,392 tons, over 70,000,000 tons came from Mesabi. During the first ten years of this century production on this range averaged about 19,000,000 tons per year; in the second and third decades it averaged over 33,000,000 tons. There was a wide fluctuation during the 1930's because of the depression, varying from a low of less than 2,000,000 tons in 1932 to a high of almost 46,000,000 in 1937. From 1940 on the rate of production was prodigious, averaging over 58,000,000 tons per year.

Such mountainous figures tell in their own way the story of the transformation of this region within six decades from an unexplored wilderness to a chain of populous communities centering around the vast open-pit mines from Embarrass to Grand Rapids, Minnesota. The early days, of course, were harsh and full of confusion. Thousands of men of a score of different nationalities poured into the region before there were any towns, before adequate housing could be provided, before any orderly life was possible. Much unrestrained brawling took place among the miners, and there was all the roughness associated with makeshift pioneering and frontier communities. Lumberjacks on sprees fought and feuded with the miners. Few of the miners could read or write, and each little nationality group spoke its own tongue in its own dialect. It is one of the miracles of American life, and a tribute to the strength of its cultural traditions, that these chaotic and disparate elements could be shaped into admirable and progressive communities in so short a time.

The mining companies themselves took the lead in improving the environment and general living conditions. The pattern set at Gwinn by Cleveland-Cliffs has already been described. The Oliver Iron Mining Company built the model village of Coleraine on the shore of Trout Lake in one of the most attractive settings on the range. The wide streets were planned by Archie Chisholm, a partner of Frank Hibbing, and laid out with a view to beauty as well as utility and were planted with trees. The public buildings were designed with the same care and the grounds artistically landscaped and planted with flowers. The company built most of the homes, constantly varying the design to avoid monotony. It financed public improvements, and provided a hospital.

Because of the immense deposits of ore, the little towns soon found themselves wealthy from the taxes paid under Minnesota law by the companies. These range towns got about 90 per cent of their income from the companies, and since the valuations on the ore properties were high, they did not have to worry about their own personal taxes to finance the heavy expenditures for local improvements. Few communities in the nation have been able to command such great municipal tax resources.

The little town of Buhl, named for a Sharon, Pennsylvania, steelmaster, happened to be in the center of a good mining district. One of the mines, the Wabigon, set an all-time record for cheap mining when a five-man crew, using an electric shovel with a 10-ton dipper, scooped up 500,000 tons of ore in two seasons. Tax money flowed in and Buhl built a magnificent high-school building which dominates the little town and towers above the rest of the skyline.

Eveleth, locally and appropriately known as "The Hill Top City," was similarly endowed. It too was in a great mining center. It had struggled along through the pioneering 1890's with its population steadily rising to 2,752. Then, as new mines came in, it jumped forward to 7,036 in 1910 and leveled off. With its mounting tax duplicate it erected fine modern school buildings and developed splendid parks for every kind of outdoor community recreation.

At the same time five miles north, Virginia, which in its maturity had dropped the "City" from its name, was surpassing Eveleth's achievements. It had burned down, with everything wiped out except two hotels, in 1900. It began afresh to build itself into its present eminence as a residential town and trading center for a wide area. It, too, lavished funds on its school system. Among other things it built a technical school and a great junior high school, complete with swimming pool, a huge and perfectly equipped auditorium and other modern appointments. In 1929 it added the big Gothic-style Roosevelt High School designed and accoutered with equal elaborateness. It added to the school staff a part-time doctor, a full-time dentist and nurse, and introduced special classes for both handicapped and gifted children. It fosters several musical organizations and provides instruction and free use of several types of instruments for the school children. It also built a $500,000 War Memorial Building for dancing in summer, skating and hockey in winter, and with clubrooms, dining room and kitchens to serve the community life.

The most lavish of all these community enterprises is at Hibbing. When Captain Frank Hibbing was helping in the 1890's to build the town which bears his name, he did not know that he was setting it on top of the greatest single deposit of ore on the range. The pits had been opened north of the town. But the open-pit operation, known as the Hull-Rust and now as the Hull-Rust-Mahoning, got bigger and bigger as the deposit was uncovered. By the close of World War I the excavations had reached the outer edge of Hibbing, clearly revealing that this rich thick deposit went right on south under the city streets and buildings. The pit had grown so deep and so close to some of the houses that the earth was beginning to cave in under them. A few abandoned houses crashed over into the pit. The Oliver Company decided to move Hibbing. It bought 40 acres of the town bordering on the mine. Then it moved the houses, including Cass Gilbert's Christ Memorial Church, the hotels, saloons and shops, and the cemetery a mile and a half away to the southeast to a new location off the ore body.

The transplantation took three years. During that period on almost any day a few houses or a building, or two at a time, were placed on rollers and towed down the streets to new foundations. It has been estimated that it cost the company many millions of dollars to clear away the old town. There are still a few of the houses remaining ghostlike in the original location to suggest a striking contrast between the old and the new community. Up to 1949, 188,993,434 tons of ore had been shipped out of the Hull-Rust and 93,853,844 tons from the adjoining Mahoning Mine.

To the spectator, standing on the observation platform and looking over into the cavernous pit, the separate mining operations are indistinguishable. It is simply one vast excavation whose dimensions are almost beyond comprehension. It covers 1,250 acres. It is three miles long. In some places it is a mile wide, in others half that distance. It is scooped out to a depth of 435 feet. It is stepped down from the surface in a series of terraces or benches which support the railroad tracks that zigzag down to the floor. Fifty-five miles of track are exposed to view. The 350-ton electric shovels, scooping up 16 tons of ore at a bite, look from this height and this distance like children's toys in a sandbox. But they are working in the greatest man-made hole in the world.

It is said that every time one of these shovels snaps up a load of iron ore it places in Hibbing's treasury about $1.25 in school taxes. The relocated city made lavish use of its income, 95 cents of each tax-dollar coming from the mines. It built a school in 1921 whose splendor and appointments are unrivaled. The cost has not been authoritatively announced, but it must have been not less than the often-mentioned $4,000,000, and possibly the $6,000,000 sometimes cited. At any rate it has, in addition to class rooms for children from kindergarten to second year junior college, a fine auditorium, library, study hall, two gymnasiums, swimming pool, indoor track, machine shops, industrial art room and equipment, a greenhouse, a beautifully outfitted home-economics division, a pipe organ—and almost everything else that should make for superior educational opportunities. The Park School, though less elaborate, is done in equal style.

Besides its schools, Hibbing has been able to afford the big War Service Memorial Building, covering a city block, with its bowling alleys, curling club quarters, and an arena for hockey or for basketball where 5,000 spectators may look on. It has six municipal parks, one of them 47 acres in extent, with municipal greenhouses to furnish flowers for the grounds and for public functions. And Hibbing, like the other towns, provided itself with hospitals and libraries, with ample public utilities, with handsome street lights, golf courses and community houses, and it paved all its streets.

With such resources at their disposal, the only wonder perhaps is that the people should have used them so largely for the public welfare. They are especially, and rightly, proud of their schools and the school system. It is a good indication that they have taken over the American faith in education and the American concern that the new generation should have better opportunities than were afforded to their fathers. The results achieved by these schools certainly have been tremendous. The polyglot nature of the speech in the earlier days, when Greek, Italian, Middle European, German, all the Scandinavian languages and many others were common in their respective groups, divided the communities sharply into small nationality groups. The schools, concentrating on English, gave the new generation a common tongue and a common experience, and the transformation from immigrants to citizens was rapidly effected.

One cannot fully understand the differential which accounts for America's supremacy without a knowledge of these iron-ore mines which rim two sides of Lake Superior. Over 2,500,000,000 tons of iron ore have been taken from these deposits, including Canadian mines and the deep mines of the Cuyuna Range which began to produce in 1911 and have shipped from 2,000,000 to 3,000,000 tons each year since 1940. We have seen the changing and advancing techniques in the underground mines as those production figures mounted. Corresponding changes were going on at the open pits. They were not radical changes in basic methods so much as they were the evolution of more efficient machinery. For the problem has always been how to strip off the overburden and haul out the ore as cheaply as possible.

The first steps, of course, were to improve the steam shovel so that it might take bigger and faster bites, and to increase the power of the locomotives and the capacity of the cars that went down into and came up from the ever-deepening and lengthening pits. Progress was steady through the years and it still continues. Small steam shovels grew into big ones. They became 300-ton machines, then 350-ton giants with 16-ton-capacity dippers. No longer limited in mobility, they were completely revolving and could move about through the pits following the seams of good ore. In due course the steam shovels gave way to the newer and bigger electric-power and Diesel shovels, and these in turn have gradually increased in size, mobility and scooping capacity. In some of the Mesabi mines a single enormous electric shovel may be seen perched on a footing of ore, reaching its long arm far out into the pit, and scooping up great quantities of loose iron ore with a huge bucket on the end of a dragline. Even in the spacious setting of an open-pit mine they look gigantic. The use of the electric shovel not only increases the capacity for work, but it eliminates the cost and the nuisance of delivering fuel and water to the steam shovels.

The evolution of transportation in the pits has been equally remarkable. The first little steam engines zig-zagged back and forth along the benches on reasonable grades pulling the ore-laden cars up to the main line. The engines, of course, grew larger and more powerful and the capacity of the ore cars increased. The pits grew longer and deeper. More track was required and more inclined benches were needed to support them as they followed the operations down through the ore body. And at the end of each bench, room had to be made for a spur and switch so that the train could reverse its direction to go on down to the next bench level. This in turn increased the length of the haul, and withheld from use a large tonnage of ore. The trains in some of the deeper mines must crawl back and forth on these terraces along the sides of the mine wall four or five times in order to climb up out of the pit with a load on grades within their power to ascend. Diesel-powered engines are now replacing the steam engines in some of the mines because they can haul still larger loads at less cost. It is not uncommon to see both types winding up and down the terraces at the same time in the same pit.

Some of the big mines, having heavy investments in track and railroad equipment, find it profitable to continue this method of hauling. In others, including the Cleveland-Cliffs Mesabi mines, two others steps have eliminated the rails entirely from the pits. The first is the introduction of rugged, heavy-duty Diesel-powered trucks to replace the railroad haul in the mines. These

remarkable vehicles can dash around through the pits
over all sorts of grades and on roadways that are comparatively cheap to construct and easy to alter as the
operations proceed. The railroad benches and the switch-
backs can be mined out. The trucks can follow the shovels
into stringers of ore which could not otherwise be mined
without handling excessive quantities of rock and waste.
They work right around these "horses of rock" following
the pay dirt like cattle cropping green grass in a boulder-
strewed meadow. They are especially effective for mining deep narrow deposits which would be practically
denied to railroad hauls.

The other great step forward was the introduction of
the conveyor-belt system at mines like the Hill-Trumbull,
the Canisteo, the Holman-Cliffs and the Hawkins mines.
Both the Hill-Trumbull and the Canisteo mines had
formerly been operated by the Oliver Iron Mining
Company, but had been abandoned and allowed to fill
up with water. They became huge lakes. The properties
were leased by Cleveland-Cliffs and its associates, the
first in 1919 and the second in 1929. The company first
mined the ore at Hill-Trumbull by shovel and railroad
methods along the ore banks above the water level. Then
it gradually pumped out the water and by 1929 the mine
was in full operation with miles of track strewed through
the pit. Something like 2,500,000,000 gallons of water
were likewise pumped out of the Canisteo pit, and the
first ore was shipped by the new operators in 1933—

mined by electric shovel. Both mines were adapted to the conveyor system. A belt conveyor was installed at Canisteo in 1939 to lift the ore directly from the pit to a new washing plant. The big trucks haul the ore from the shovel to the hopper in the pit, and it is delivered in an endless stream to the hopper at the washing plant. The same general system, introduced at Hill-Trumbull in 1942, likewise discarded all tracks in this pit. The full transition, effected in space of a single decade, is illustrated by the work at these two mines.

The same process was applied with equal efficiency and economy to the task of removing the overburden. The layer of surface material lying on top of the ore body varies in thickness, as we have noted, from a few feet to 100 feet or more. In a few of the mines where it was unprofitable to remove the heavier overburden, the ore was extracted by a form of underground mining. But modern methods of stripping and hauling make it possible to remove greater yardage from deposits that are rich and extensive. These methods were made possible by the introduction of draglines and conveyor belts.

Around some of the mines it is a problem to find a place to put the waste material. It has been piled up like young mountains over vast acreages along the range just off the ore body. It creates a terrain that is at once both desolate and strangely alive with activity on a scale that challenges the imagination. At the Hill-Trumbull pit alone, approximately a million cubic yards of overburden were stripped and moved off the ore each year during the early 1920's. When we consider that operations of this kind have been going on all along the 125 miles of the range, we get some concept of the amount of earth that has been moved in the last 60 years. Most of it was handled by steam shovel and railroad dump cars. But there is an economic limit to the distance a truck or a steam engine can haul this kind of load, just as there is a space problem to find a dumping ground around some of the crowded mining districts.

The modern belt-conveyor system has given a solution. It is shown dramatically at the Canisteo Mine near Coleraine and Bovey on the western sector of the Mesabi. The only available dump site for this stripping operation was about 4,000 feet to the east in an open space north of Bovey. Between it and the mine were houses, high-ways and railroads and it would have been economically impossible to haul the overburden over the long and tortuous route which trucks would have to follow. There was no place whatever for railroad tracks. The company installed a conveyor-stripping system approximately 6,000 feet long in 1948. It rises from the pit and proceeds to the dumping ground in four flights. It goes under one railroad through a tunnel, then over two tracks of another road on a bridge, then under a highway through another tunnel, over still another highway on a bridge, and finally crawls up a slope to the disposal grounds. This 36-inch belt system delivers a steady stream of stripping from mine to dump.

The unusually deep overburden is first scooped up by a huge shovel with a large dragline and an eight-yard bucket. It is whisked up into a screening plant where all the lumps over eight inches in size are removed on a vibrating screen. This big stuff is delivered to a pocket at the end of the screening plant and is hauled away by truck. All the rest of it is fed into a short shuttle conveyor which dumps it onto the long field belt to be delivered nearly a mile away to the disposal ground. Here at the end of its route over and under all obstacles it is received by a "trailing conveyor" mounted on crawler trucks, and a specially devised stacker. This stacker has a 104-foot boom, and it can swing in an arc of 180 degrees to spread the material over a wide area. As the pile of waste creeps out into the field, the stacker moves forward along with the trailing conveyor. This simple and highly systematic technique has made it possible to develop as an open pit properties which were formerly considered strictly underground operations.

The Mesabi Range excited the wonder of the world because it had so much iron ore so close to the surface; ore which could be mined in open pits and shipped directly to the furnaces. But 60 years of exploitation for the national economy, including the heavy demands of two world wars, have sharply reduced the supply of direct-shipping ore. This has led to a more intensive search for other deposits, and to the development of new fields in various parts of the world. The ore beds thus far located are relatively far from the consuming furnaces—in Ontario, Liberia and Venezuela. It is generally assumed that the future needs of the nation for iron ore will be supplemented from these new areas, despite the transportation difficulties which must be overcome.

There are other considerations, however, which point toward the continued productivity of Mesabi into an indefinite future. The range has certainly reduced, but by no means exhausted, its supply of direct-shipping ore. More important is the relation of these bodies of richer ore to the rest of the deposits somewhat leaner in iron content. There are almost incalculable tons of good ore which cannot be used in its present natural state. In fact we have been exceedingly prodigal in our recovery of the Mesabi ore. The mining methods have corresponded roughly to the early logging operations of a generation or two ago, before forest management was thought of, which slashed wastefully through the great forests of the Northwest Territory taking out the white and yellow pine and scorning the hemlock. In much the same fashion the great shovels on the Mesabi have rooted along the rich seams, ignoring or casting aside the formations which could not be used in their natural state. Some of the material of low iron content in more recent years has been heaped up in vast dumps like river bluffs over thousands of acres of open fields near the mines in the expectation that someday a method will be found to use it.

There are other enormous beds of ore which fall just below the 51 per cent of iron content necessary for direct shipping. So long as there was plenty of rich ore to be had, there was not much point in bothering with the leaner stuff. On the other hand it seemed folly to ignore it as waste simply because it was mixed up with a lot of paint rock and silica. The American scientific mind was intrigued and challenged to find a practical method of separating the ore from the impurities.

The Hill-Trumbull and Canisteo Mine region on the western Mesabi offered good material for experiments in concentration. The deposit was composed for the most part of alternating layers of high-grade ore and very fine sand. Some successful experiments in separating them had been conducted from 1901 to 1904. In 1905 the Oliver Iron Mining Company took up the investigation. In 1906 it erected an experimental plant near the Canisteo Mine to try the method of washing the ore. With the aid of manufacturers a series of machines was designed to crush, classify and separate the materials. Following up the experiments, this company built a washing plant on Trout Lake near Coleraine in 1909-1910. Since that time many new improvements and refinements have been introduced.

In 1920, the year after the lease of the Hill-Trumbull property was acquired by Cleveland-Cliffs and its associates, they proceeded to erect a washing plant two miles southeast of the mine with a crusher to break up the chunks of ore and sand, and a washer building connected with it by a belt conveyor. The wash ore was delivered to the plant by train. Another washing plant was built at the Holman-Cliffs Mine, one at the Canisteo, and one at the Hawkins Mine. A new one at the Sargent Mine was opened in 1950.

These plants perform three types of beneficiation. In the first class of merchantable ore the mined material runs usually about 51 per cent or higher in high-grade iron content and 14 per cent or lower in silica. In general the merchantable material mined is earthy in structure, containing chunks, some of them from two to three feet in diameter, much too large for use. This raw material is then passed over a six-inch screen to separate out the larger chunks. These in turn are then crushed to six inches or smaller and are ready to be fed to the blast furnaces. It is the simplest means of beneficiation.

Treatment of the wash ores is more complicated. In this material the coarser particles are high grade, but the finer ones are mixed with silica. The crude ore comes up from the pit on the conveyor to the washing plant, where it is crushed to pass through a screen with 1½ inch openings. The ore lumps that are between 1½ and ⅝ inches are finished material and can be directed to the cars for shipping. The smaller particles must then be treated to remove the silica. They are carried from the screen to a mechanical classifier pool, of rake or spiral type, where they are washed. The pool density, together with the velocity of the water, washes the silica out over the weir to be floated to the tailing ponds, while the iron sinks to the bottom and is conveyed out to the cars to be shipped. By this method from 50 to 75 per cent of the crude material by weight is recovered for use.

There is still a third kind of material that can be treated. It is known as retreat or jig ore, and it requires a maximum amount of beneficiation to extract the shipping-grade iron ore. All the particles of this material, regardless of size, contain silica to the amount of 14 per cent or more. The ore is reduced to particles under 1¼ inches in size. It is then placed in a heavy-media separator pool. Silica has a specific gravity of 2.65 and the iron particles have a specific gravity of 4.50. The pool is filled with finely ground ferro-silicon metal and water to form a medium of the right density (2.90 to 3.00), to float off the waste while the heavier iron sinks to the bottom, like a handful of wood chips and gravel thrown into a pool of water. The lighter waste particles are conveyed from the plant and stockpiled for possible future beneficiation. The residual ore, now washed clean, goes out of the pool into the cars to be shipped to the furnaces.

Cleveland-Cliffs was one of the first companies on the range to adopt this modern conservation practice for utilizing ores which had previously been considered discard. It has even carried the process one step further in one of the most interesting examples of conservation on the entire range. The old Holman-Cliffs tailings basin was a tract of swamp land over three-fifths of a mile long and a fifth of a mile wide. Since this area was not an inclosed basin, a dike was built along three sides of the tract to contain the tailings and prevent them from finding their way into Trout Lake. This dumping ground gradually filled up with washed-out waste from the early washing-plant operations. But the waste contained a fair percentage of unrecovered iron-ore particles. The company built a special beneficiation plant on the edge of this basin, and is putting the old tailings through an ingenious process to separate the remaining ore from the final and ultimate waste.

These remarkable developments are pointing the way to new concepts for utilizing the leaner ores on the Mesabi. During the year 1948, 21.54 per cent of all the iron ore shipped from Minnesota mines was beneficiated in one form or another, most of it, of course, by the simpler wash methods. That was 18,000,000 out of the total of 69,000,000 tons. In 1906, when over 25,000,000 tons were shipped from this district, not a single ton was beneficiated or concentrated. The more complex heavy-media process now accounts for over 1,500,000 tons annually. Experiments are being carried on extensively in laboratories and pilot plants at the mines and elsewhere to improve the methods of treating the ore and reducing the cost. It is inconceivable that they will not be successful. And they will be applied to the 30 per cent iron "formation materials" which now lie there adjacent to the direct shipping mines in such stupendous volume that geologists estimate them in many billions of tons. If we run out of usable iron ore on the Mesabi Range, it will be due to the failure of American science and mechanical skill. In view of present progress, that seems unlikely. Worry over the exhaustion of the supply of ore is premature.

| 19 |

ORE FLEET AND WATERWAY

The vital link between the iron rim of Lake Superior and the furnaces that border the lower lakes is the Great Lakes waterway. It is impossible to exaggerate the supreme importance of this thousand-mile-long ship road. It is a geological miracle indeed that it should have been formed right in the heart of the American continent, that at one end there should be these deposits of iron ore, and that in close proximity to the other end there should be the great coal seams. And it is, perhaps, another kind of miracle that concentrated along or near Lake Erie there should be so many skilled workmen, so many railroads and highways, and such a diversity of consuming industries. It is hard to conceive how these mountainous tonnages of iron ore could have been transported without the waterway and the great freighters which sail back and forth over it, or how they could have been used effectively without the coal and limestone which lie in such abundance near the steel mills.

As the Mesabi Range came in and the tonnage mounted, bigger ships were required to haul the ore. They were forthcoming. But their carrying capacity was also dependent on the width and depth in the harbors and in the channels connecting the chain of Great Lakes: St. Marys River, the Sault, St. Clair River, Lake St. Clair and Detroit River. The rivers and Lake St. Clair were dredged and deepened as the drafts increased. The big Poe Lock of 1896, 800 by 100 by 22 feet, accommodated the upward rush of the 1890's and the first few years of the new century. Around 12,000,000 tons passed through the Sault in 1897; over 38,000,000 in 1906.

The new Davis Canal and Lock was started in 1907 and opened to traffic in 1914 in time to take care of the demands of World War I which reached close to 65,000,-000 tons in 1916. The Sabin Lock was begun in 1911 and opened in 1919 while the demand was still running high. Both locks were 1,350 feet long, 80 feet wide, and 24½ feet deep. And once more, in 1942, when over 92,000,000 tons went through the Sault to meet the urgencies of World War II, still another lock was needed. Christened the MacArthur Lock, it was opened on June 26, 1943. It is 800 feet long, 80 feet wide, and 30 feet deep. The little schooner *Columbia* had locked through the first canal on August 17, 1855, bearing her 120 tons of ore from Marquette. On August 17, 1949, the 620-foot *Champlain* was lowered through the MacArthur Lock bearing 14,909 tons. One century had elapsed between the launching of these two ships.

The iron-ore companies, working with the lake ship-builders, had accomplished this great transformation. It corresponded to the evolution from the small steam shovels to the giant electric machines, from the horse carts to the big steel dump cars, from the little steam locomotive *Sebastopol* to the modern Diesels. The ore-producing companies, as we have seen, developed their own fleets of carriers. The ships themselves are more or less standard, and are very much alike. They were steadily lengthened, widened and deepened, and their carrying capacity kept mounting. The giant vessels of the 3,000-ton class were obsolete by 1904. They were gradually supplanted by a new generation represented by the first *William G. Mather*, later called the *Sheadle*. This ship had a capacity of 10,700 tons and a 60-foot beam, and there was only one lock at the Sault at the time big enough to receive her.

Still bigger vessels were needed during World War I and the years immediately following. The 13,000-ton *Pontiac* came out in 1917, and the *Frontenac*, of the same capacity, in 1923. Two years later the second *William G. Mather*, flagship of the Cleveland-Cliffs fleet, was brought out with a carrying capacity of 13,500 tons. She could carry a total of 500,000 tons in one full shipping season. There were only a half dozen ships of her class on the lakes in the 1920's. In fact, for the next 17 years she was the last word in ship design, propulsion, navigation equipment and crew accommodations.

These new ships were not only efficient carriers, but they were designed as a well-appointed home afloat for the crew. Back in the old sailing ships of the 1870's the men lived in an unsanitary little forecastle and their living conditions were primitive. Paint and loose gear were piled forward with the sailors. Captain Thomas E. Murray, recalling these days, said that "the air was so bad a lamp would scarcely burn, and there was not a single room sufficiently tight to keep water out in a head sea or when it rained, and when you encountered heavy seas or it rained you went to bed with your oil skins to keep dry." Most of the sailors, he said, were from the British Isles, with a sprinkling of Scandinavians and a few men from the Orkney Islands.

The modern lake freighter by comparison is a luxury liner. There are pleasant staterooms for the captain and the mates, and for the chief engineer and assistants; and ample and comfortable quarters for all the crew. There are bathrooms, shower rooms, and recreation quarters. The rooms are well lighted and air-conditioned. Hallways in the afterdeck cabin make it unnecessary to go on deck to report to the engine room or to enter the dining rooms. A tunnel running the full length of the ship gives the men a protected passage between the texas house forward and the afterdeck cabin. The galley and mess halls are worthy of a good hotel, and the food is top quality and abundant. Orange juice, fresh vegetables and beefsteak have taken the place of corn beef, salt pork, prunes and hardtack of the old days. The refrigerators and cooking utensils are stainless steel. Everything is spotlessly clean. Wages are high and the work is not too hard.

The fleet as developed through the 1920's was more than adequate for the lean years of the 1930's. During that period the shipyards on the lakes were idle much of the time, and no new freighters were launched. The sudden big call for iron ore by World War II at the beginning of the 1940's found the fleet inadequate to the demand. Five new ships with carrying capacity of from 15,000 to 17,500 tons went into service with the Pittsburgh Steamship Company in 1942. They were followed by 16 more, built for the Maritime Commission, each capable of hauling the equivalent of about 260 modern railroad freight cars. They were sold to the various iron-ore companies as a part of a program again to modernize the Great Lakes fleet. They have a one-piece-unit hatch cover and a traveling crane which can remove or cover the 18 hatches in about 13 minutes. The *Champlain*, which, along with the *Cadillac*, went to Cleveland-Cliffs, has the new cruiser stern which gives her the advantage of one-half a mile an hour more speed than the ships of conventional design.

The pilothouses, equipped with all the latest navigation aids, are spacious and agreeable rooms. The engine rooms have automatic stokers, and a constant steam pressure is maintained merely by the turning of valves. The old-time fireman standing his watch with a shovel and sweat cloth, and hitting the fires regularly with a "wabash" of coal to keep a head of steam, is rapidly passing from the lakes. The fireman on one of these modern freighters may have a cloth in his hand, but he will be using it to polish a gauge, not to wipe sweat from his forehead. The fire room on these latest vessels is often the coolest part of the engine and boilerrooms.

Manned and equipped in this fashion, the ships make their scheduled voyages back and forth from the loading docks to the lower lake ports like clockwork. They are directed by radio-telephone from the central offices in Cleveland. They not only bring iron ore down the lakes, but they carry coal on their upbound voyages. The coal business, therefore, figures heavily in the total enterprise of iron-ore mining and transportation. It grew into major importance around the turn of the century. It was spurred not only by the development of the iron ranges but also by the rapid growth of both rural and urban population in the near northwest which needed an adequate and dependable supply of fuel. Cleveland-Cliffs, the oldest of the ore companies, foresaw an increasing demand by the steel industry for by-product coal and, as a protection for that demand, acquired its first coal lands in Pennsylvania in 1909. The Mather Collieries, organized in 1919 with Cleveland-Cliffs as a one-third partner, took over this original property and the two adjoining tracts owned by the other participating interests. Now owned equally by Steel Company of Canada and Cleveland-Cliffs, this operation at Mather, Greene County, Pennsylvania, is equipped with a most modern tipple and washing plant with coal reserve sufficient to assure production at the present rate for some twenty additional years.

The coal consumption during World War I was tremendous. In order to assure upbound pay loads for its vessels, Cleveland-Cliffs acquired additional coal lands with three operating mines in West Virginia; and, in 1919, it organized a Coal Department. Its coal business, supplemented by purchases and by agency arrangements with coal producers, reached a peak in excess of 5,000,-000 tons for the year 1948. The West Virginia operation proved unprofitable, and it was disposed of in 1930. Its output was replaced and augmented by that of various other producers for which the company acts as exclusive selling agent. In the years since 1922, the company has acquired a modern coal-storage dock and equipment at Green Bay, Wisconsin, the controlling interest in a dock and equipment at Escanaba, Michigan, and, through wholly owned subsidiaries, a large dock and equipment at Duluth, Minnesota, and a vessel-fueling dock at Port Huron, Michigan.

The opening and closing of the shipping season have become seasonal ceremonies. As the winter begins to close in, the ships are inspected to see whether any major repairs will be needed. If they are, the vessel will be moored for the winter in the repair yards of the lowest and best bidder to be made ready for the opening of the new season. Vessels that need drydocking are laid up in ports that have these facilities. Others carry down a load of storage grain and moor in one of the elevator ports. Some are anchored in ports where they will be available for early spring loading. And some are berthed in Cleveland and other ports while the lakes are closed.

This is not a simple matter of tying the ship up somewhere. The water levels and the nature of the lake bottom must be reckoned with. Strong southwest winds will lower Lake Erie as much as seven and a half feet below datum at Toledo and raise it as high as nine and a half feet at Buffalo. An easterly gale will lower the level at Buffalo as much as four feet and raise it 12 at Toledo. The ports between will strike an average of these fluctuations. The nature of the lake bottom, whether it is rock or sand, makes a difference, and many things may cause trouble among the moored vessels. It takes about a week to put away all the equipment and furnishings and to wash out the ship thoroughly. It requires about a month to overhaul and fit out the ship for the new season.

As March comes in and the days lengthen and warm, a certain restlessness begins to seize the harbors. Reports on the structure and depth of the ice at the Sault and in the St. Marys River are scanned with attention and predictions are made as to the date for the clearing of the channels. In the meantime the chief engineers and their crews are sent to the ships, together with the stewards and their departments. The main engines and auxiliaries are thoroughly overhauled and boilers fired. In about two weeks' time the mates and deck crews are put aboard and all deck equipment and navigating instruments are put in order. When this work is done, the masters report to their ships and they are ready to sail.

When conditions are favorable, the ingeniously equipped and designed icebreakers fare forth to break a passage for the freighters. They ram the ice field, crush the sheets with their weight, clear the road for the vessels, and the season is under way. But the first weeks may be fraught with danger. Gales on Lake Huron and Lake Superior may pile up formidable windrows of thick ice to imperil the ships and a sudden freeze may trap them in the ice in Whitefish Bay or off the Lake Superior and Lake Michigan harbors.

The annals of the Great Lakes are filled with the hazardous experiences of men and ships caught in the ice. The spring of 1917 was memorable. The *Munising* sailed out of Cleveland on April 18 to carry a load of coal to Marquette. She passed through the Sault without trouble and continued through Whitefish Bay amid broken ice. The next day these ice lanes closed. She encountered some solid ice in Lake Superior, but she broke through it without difficulty. Seven miles out of Marquette, however, she struck a heavy field of windrowed ice which wedged her in so tight that she could not move. Day after day she was trapped there. Food ran short. Five men took the desperate chance of crawling over the ice jams, in some places wading through slush, in others jumping across cracks, to reach Marquette and bring help to the ship and her crew. Other steamers finally cut through to her with food. A south wind ultimately freed her from the grip of ice, and the *Munising* reached port on the morning of May 16.

Such experiences used to be rather common. In more recent times, with ice-breaking cutters, ship-to-shore communication, and with the constant and detailed reports on weather and ice conditions coming in at frequent intervals and the caution of the operators to prevent the ships from being trapped, these occurrences are rare. The ships are held until the lakes are open, and when the season begins, the movement of ore is continuous until the ice again closes over after seven or eight months.

At the beginning of this Century of Iron, pig iron production of the nation was only 500,000 tons a year, smelters and forges produced raw iron and crude steel in limited quantity, and William Kelly had not yet startled the countryside with his attempt at the Bessemer Process. The nation was growing apace, but it had not begun to throb with the vital strength which flowed into it when iron ore began to pour down the Great Lakes to be fashioned into steel in the Bessemer Converter to meet the needs of an expanding country. This ore made the steel rails for the network of railroads, for the great machines and transportation equipment, for the presses, stamping machines, cranes, conveyors, locomotives, cars, automobiles and trucks on which the prosperity of the nation depends. And in time of war it has provided a basic material for defense.

Taken altogether it is a stupendous, complex and interlinking operation from mine shaft and open pit to the furnaces; the ultimate product of the years of growing experience and vision. It is a monumental tribute to the generations of men from all walks of life who have brought these great resources from an unexplored wilderness to their central place in the structure of American supremacy in the space of one full century.

ACKNOWLEDGMENTS
AND BIBLIOGRAPHICAL NOTE

ACKNOWLEDGMENTS
AND BIBLIOGRAPHICAL NOTE

IN MANY years of travel about the Great Lakes it has been my privilege to talk with people of every variety of interest in this remarkable region. All of them have contributed in some fashion to the making of this book. I am especially indebted to Ernest L. Kirkwood, who made a study tour of the Lake Superior iron ranges with me, who has aided me constantly in research problems, and has put at my disposal much rich and original source material on the history and development of the iron-ore industry.

I express great appreciation to Edward B. Greene and Alexander C. Brown and their staff of The Cleveland-Cliffs Iron Company for all their aid in the preparation of the manuscript; and for the hospitality and generous aid given by C. J. Stakel and his staff at Ishpeming, Michigan, and W. A. Sterling of Hibbing, who showed me every detail of the complex operation of iron-ore mining in Minnesota; to R. A. Brotherton, who has delved extensively into the early history and lore of the Marquette region; and to Captain C. N. Bedell for his personal instruction in the operation and navigation of a Great Lakes freighter.

The sheer volume of source material on this phase of American history is immense. Much of it is scientific and technical, the accumulation of several generations of study by geologists, mineralogists, mining experts, scientists and technicians of all kinds who have labored in this field. I have drawn heavily on their somewhat dusty volumes, chiefly the annual *Proceedings of the Lake Superior Mining Institute*, the reports of the Commissioner of Mineral Statistics of the State of Michigan, the annual reports of the Minnesota Geological and Natural History Survey, the *Proceedings of the Lake Superior Mines Safety Council*, the trade journals of the iron industry, the minutes of the directors of the early companies, and the newspapers and journals of the period. Invaluable material is to be found scattered through this huge library, like small veins of direct-shipping ore in a vast body of surrounding taconite.

Most of the single-volume studies have been mentioned in the text: Houghton's reports, Burt's field books, etc., and Ralph D. Williams' *The Honorable Peter White*, which tells the story of that colorful pioneer at Marquette, and *The Autobiography of Captain Alexander McDougall*. Allan Nevins has a full and well-documented treatment of Rockefeller's Mesabi venture in his *John D. Rockefeller*. Stewart H. Holbrook's *Iron Brew* is a rich, colorful and human book on the story of ore and steel. Paul De Kruif dealt with the Merritts in his *Seven Iron Men*. Joe Russell Whitaker wrote a fine dissertation on *Negaunee, Michigan: An Urban Center Dominated by Iron Mining*. There is much miscellaneous information in the American Lakes Series of volumes dealing with the Great Lakes.